Monkey Puzzles 2

More of the best cryptic crosswords

Araucaria

Atlantic Books
London

• *Araucaria's preferred source for alternative spellings and usages is Chambers Twentieth Century Dictionary*

First published in 2004 by Atlantic Books on behalf of Guardian Newspapers Ltd. Atlantic Books is an imprint of Grove Atlantic Ltd.

10 9 8 7 6 5 4 3 2 1

A CIP catalogue record for this book is available from the British Library

ISBN 1 84354 261 7

Printed in Great Britain by
Mackays of Chatham Limited

Design by Liz McCabe
Cover design by Ghost

Grove Atlantic Ltd
Ormond House
26-27 Boswell Street
London WC1N 3JZ

Monkey Puzzles

Across

9 Tailpiece, a pianissimo conclusion on time (9)
10 Original to the Spanish post (5)
11 Run fast and talk a lot? It makes one cry (4,3)
12 The wit that burns (7)
13 It gets hit on the finger (4)
14 Performance with strings attached (6,4)
16 Something written (7)
17 Glen and sea blend in Africa (7)
19 Dog and Dirt, by George North, the boor! (10)
22 A bit to play (4)
24 Knock without effect: it's fast (7)
25 Noted doctor trampled under foot (7)
26 Strange — that's always (5)
27 ... far from what the Raven said (9)

Down

1 Tea, perhaps, at ten, with meat monopoly at Epsom (9,6)
2 A religious nobleman loses nothing to a beekeeper (8)
3 Jones in a single shot (5)
4 It's the fool in me that would use a rubber (8)
5 Storm centre? (6)
6 Offensive gun in list? (9)
7 A shilling a hundred comes in with change (6)
8 London underground passage with dark sides? (9,6)
15 Don's cruel, perverted and a villain (9)
17 Change proves it playful (8)
18 Watch the watcher? (5,3)
20 Sound piece of writing? (6)
21 Chap with a 16 off the Caribbean (6)
23 To care about gold is crooked (5)

1

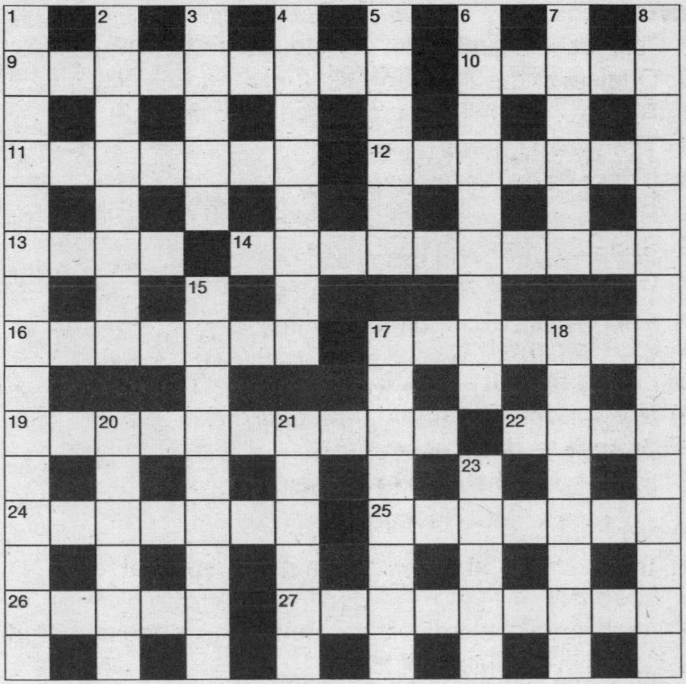

The solutions to O and C run consecutively across, as do those to H, W, A and M. The rest should be entered wherever they will fit, jigsaw-wise. Letters are used for cross-referencing in the same way that numbers are used in a normal puzzle.

A See W and M
B For paint and afterthought to muscle (6)
C See O
D For jam: it's M A in this puzzle (6)
E For noises off, results of chattels (7)
F For Lowland Scot in Irish battles (6)
G For Christmas pate? Safe to go? (5,3)
H,W Were O and J — or no? (7,3,4)
I For drive this month in carat seen (8)
J For Nap's pure Latin Grecian queen (7)
K For speech Horatio did deliver (4,2,5)
L For river's feeble love for river (7)
M,A J and O, or else their daughter (6,3,5)
N For group reporting from Freshwater? (4,4)
O,C L excused by Freud resolved (7,7)
P Word-ending, pig! Fox isn't involved (10)
Q For Durward, saint of US prison (7)
R Discern a change — withdraw permission (7)
S Brought O to fame, the puzzling brute (6)
T For PTO, a tasty root (6)
U Won't soon be M, not looking out (11)
V For green: one free, one front about (8)
W,A For folk: when did I calf? (4,3,5)
X For shrew, Socratic better half (8)
Y For snowman: still you add one on (4)
Z For saint in lake, sired James and John (7)

2

Across

1 Large single guest, no saint, near exhaustion (7)
5 Mail male? (7)
9 Melodramatically caught as a clue to "gratin"? (4,1,3,2,1,4)
10 Cat of little weight (5)
11 Great to do something better and fast (9)
12 Transport operations call in abroad too much (9)
14 Bitch's *idée fixe*? (5)
15 I obtained a second, not without prejudice (5)
16 Revolutionary morals met in a whirl (9)
18 Back kitchen equipment? Change places (9)
21 Put off a green (5)
22 It means more decimally, if I can, without a model 10 (15)
23 Left-wing president of the cinema? (7)
24 Letter turning green in mid table (7)

Down

1 Quarrel after bomb burst? (4,3)
2 Assumed gratitude and knowledge uttered without bombast (5,3,7)
3 Serious record — it may be for sailors (6-3)
4 As before without d? (5)
5 Clipper in trouble at source (9)
6 Householder's poles aren't strong (5)
7 Red king, great man, supplies fruit and veg trade (6,9)
8 Sleep hath other distillates (7)
13 People are doubly sympathetic (9)
14 In time one's standard becomes different (9)
15 Playwright on river dam? (7)
17 Playtime, perhaps, sticks a prong into me (7)
19 Two circles per Beatle (5)
20 Man banished from former French island (5)

3

Across

9 Their charges suggest fleecing (9)
10 Air from 3 (5)
11 What eats cooked ham inside on the floor? (4,3)
12 Indian finds much of 2 fashionable (7)
13 Habits on the roads? (4)
14 The Wife of Bath felt embarrassed when the Queen came in (6,4)
15 Russian girl in distraction at a shark (7)
17,22 Paper involved in strong-arm activity? (7,4)
19 Return of the pig, keeping me company for a short time (10)
22 See 17
23 Notice first given to the Navy with part of the RAF around (7)
24 Singularly the student digs may be Turkish (7)
26 See 2
27 Sole punishment for bachelors getting a model in trouble (9)

Down

1 Indication of something worthless afoot (1,5,2,3,4)
2,26 9 24: in the 17 across, 9,23 (3,3,2,5)
3 Arbitrary objective of Western man? (4)
4 In the nursery the main cause of a 12 (8)
5 Liveliness is the making of a priest (6)
6 Forest officer upsets priest before doctor's round (8)
7 Illegal bowler, say, at polo (6)
8 Biblical metamorphosis of a naturist ring? (15)
16 Holy place: it's scary, maybe (8)
17 Writer of laments gets assent when it's damp outside (8)
18 It's essential for a tin product to get a big return (8)
20 Motorway madness isn't really there (6)
21 African politician with refined oratorical powers in the Middle East (6)
25 Put down face upwards (4)

4

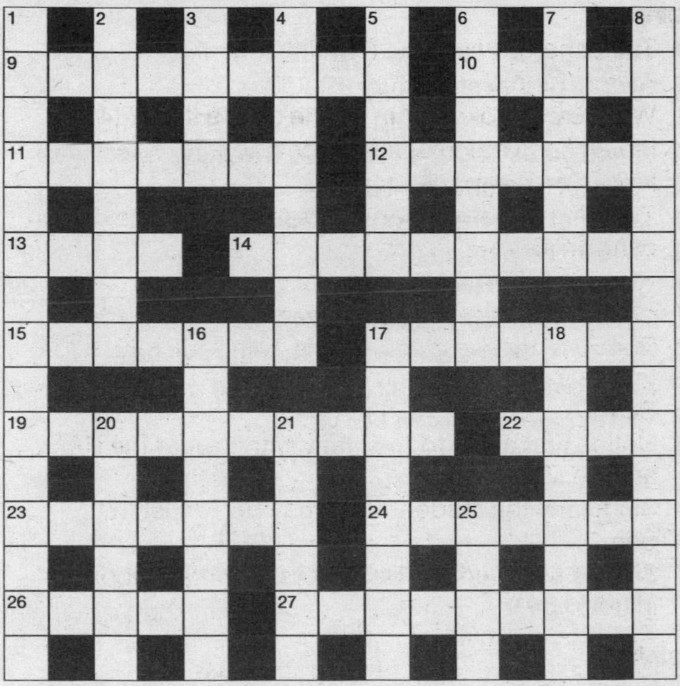

Across

7 Set of three — shall we dance? (8)
9 Yellow bird, first century (6)
10 A number in support in the centre (4)
11 Make notes about a madman wreaking havoc (10)
12 Ruler of French locality (6)
14 Unusual repartee about a partridge? (4,4)
15 Dive in, be a brick! (6)
17 Stick a bill at this point (6)
20 It keeps on shooting the parrot (8)
22 Put in a box and sent to another station (6)
23 Correct transposition of the G in the melody (10)
24 Girl's maternal instincts? (4)
25 Look out for sailors under the ground (6)
26 To the childless children are a headache (8)

Down

1 Stones put round well away from protector Walesa (8)
2 Potato digger (4)
3 Service as a relief between races (3,3)
4 NB, get the tax to come down (8)
5 The wrong way to tease bad men: they will mug you (10)
6 O'Casey at church, seeking the supernatural? (6)
8 Am I not thorough with chips? (6)
13 Railwayman arranging 3? (10)
16 The pollen effect, by C______te Yonge? (8)
18 They keep to themselves before small creatures (8)
19 Deserter among soldiers goes free (6)
21 Catch a lot of partners going up (6)
22 Turn up nothing when you start in a feeble way (6)
24 Measure food, say (4)

5

Across

1 Complete with needle? (3-2)
4 Composer spreads her wings ... (8)
8 ... in regret, having a brief year in the black after luck on the turf (8,2,4)
10 To maintain a road, don't go near it! (4,4)
11 ______ then I, then O, then U, goddess (6)
12 Push one boat out and put the tiller over (5-4)
15 One such as I, quietly in his resting place (5)
17 Ancient Britons coming in twice nightly (5)
18 Make a show at painting a hydrogen element (4,5)
19 Composer in short breaks ... (6)
21 ... starting to shingle her hair ... (8)
24 ... Cy's tail's turned, having turned tale (5,2,7)
25 Kindly treat our army to nothing French on top of Dunkirk (8)
26 Foxy drink? (5)

Down

1 Get off after industrial action and don't keep it dark (6,1,5)
2 Corset we put round Harry Black (5-4)
3 Food to get over first (5)
4 Sponsor in the First Person? (9)
5 See 23
6 Dress for the skilled to 23 in (9)
7 Accustom a 5 union that's getting about (5)
9 Provide cat's meat for the pool? (4,3,5)
13 One of the last in gratitude to one person borrowed from (4-5)
14 Bought a pudding without the right to hunt (9)
16 Not exactly half-baked old pair be blowed! (9)
20 Burning explosive is flexible (5)
22 A sort of cook? (5)
23,5 It suggests hepatitis: don't touch! (4,4)

6

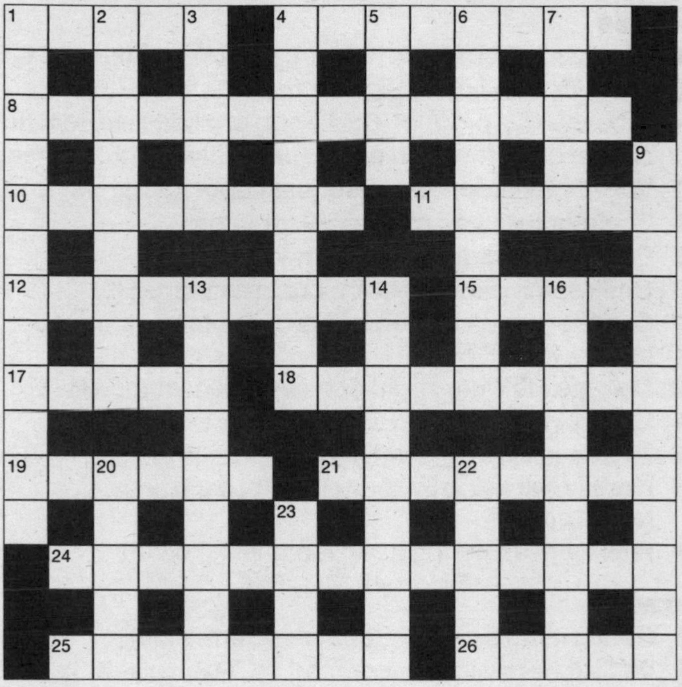

Across

1 Glasses lie from back to front, first taken from pubs (8)
5 Black or blue flower, say, for the rock with 6 (6)
9 American fur product, badly cut, provides life-rent (8)
10 Return of rent with an enclosure dealing with leather (6)
12 Vulgar presumption consequent upon dictatorship? (4,7)
15 Sculptor followed by pickle? (5)
17 Chief priest in dry church drew sound (9)
18 Cook some pie: it must be put in a nutshell (9)
19 Change of polarisation brings mountainous country into flower (5)
20 Maker's attribute could achieve nice incomes (11)
24 One point is for a god (6)
25 Maybe there's no point in a smile on a painting (4,4)
26 Northerner going East and South: Japanese robe's no less (6)
27 Fuel went up during keen reorganisation (8)

Down

1 Spring lamb's progenitor makes terms (10)
2 9 10s (pre-decimal) were, as 11s, 1 down (4,3,3)
3 Roughly spoken little creature (5)
4 With a bit of luck, young creature shares in learned works (12)
6 Cautious sort of bids for the whirlpool with 5 (9)
7,8 The street may be short English 3, not short measure (4,4)
11 A merry type, 20, on the telegraph (7,5)
13 Tree to put brush in? (10)
14 Debase mature fruit of a tree (10)
16 Mongolise mixed coinage (9)
21 The compiler's having a try at the last stage (5)
22,23 Unconvincing 11 (very!) needing help (4,4)

7

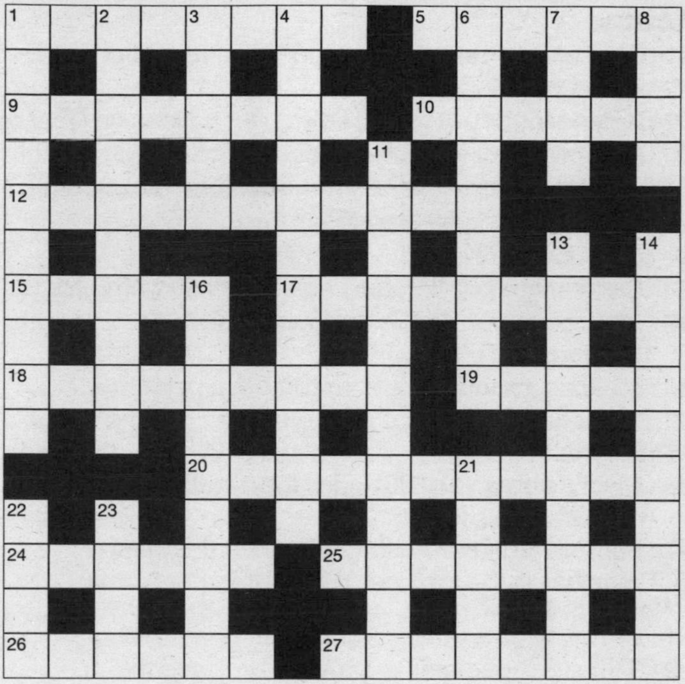

Across

1 Eaten all you can? Drink wine — we're 100 per cent behind you (4,7)
9 Before Monday morning I must get a cleaner (7)
10 City of wine, or small southeast Asian ring (7)
11 Anonymous letter saying goodbye, maybe in 10 (9)
12 Ash pale after rosy start (5)
13 Music firm? (4)
14 Opening of 6 5 or 20, perhaps, but not Twelfth Night (5,5)
16 Continued with 12 19s and walked (4,2,4)
19 13 with cape or island (4)
21 Musical turn with little electromotive power (5)
22 For culture I'm using a network (in a cow, the same as 8) (9)
24 Ghost's demand of 20 — for even-getting some might express it (7)
25 Home guard for French girlfriend in the West (7)
26 It can hardly be the age of enlightenment, when there's no news (5,6)

Down

1 Clan gatherings reminiscent of the Borgias? (6,9)
2 Material for a call in England (5)
3 Language for a call in wails, perhaps (7)
4 Store up trouble for inconstant deity (7)
5 See 6
6,5 11 and 4: for 20, 24 16 across (3,3,9,2,6)
7 Big dining chair for Doone (6)
8 Beekeeper's hat? (6)
15 Theoretical negative to Holy Island and Loch? (8)
16 Cutting short of what are in every port for sailors is monstrous (6)
17 Not Smith's own signature? (7)
18 Girl taking nearly half the box seat, I'm on the bed, probably (7)
20 Village prince (6)
23 Sacking on these is quite likely (5)

8

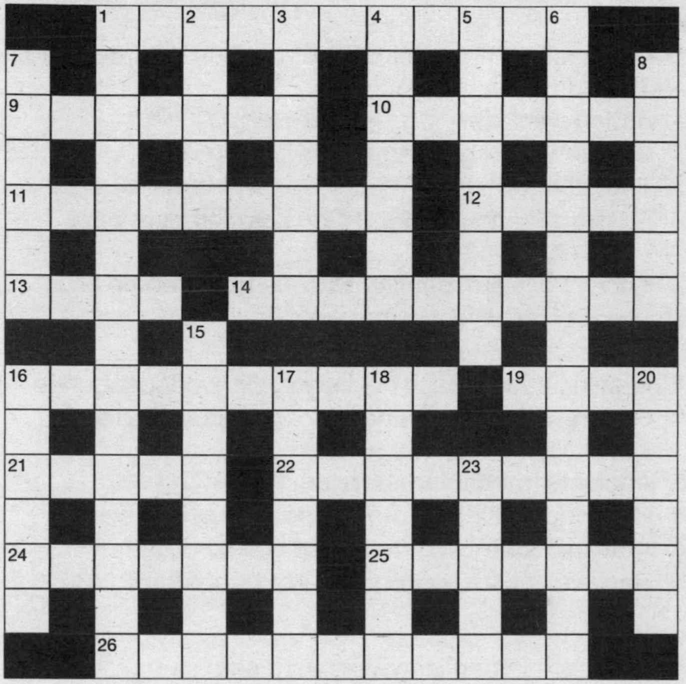

Across

1 Given religious experience through Iris Murdoch novel? That's fighting talk! (5,2,3,4)
9 Action shrouds song — so it's late (7)
10 Old composer gets home awfully tired (7)
11 Take another's part? You surprise me! (5)
12 Before a French exclamation I am father to busy Lizzie (9)
13 Ancient city etc, back with soda water bottle (9)
14 The French have a dirty look (5)
15 Prone to falsehood? (5)
17 A sailor of high class and style, with independence (9)
20 Urge revolution on rally, perhaps, according to custom (9)
22 Ancient king with artist in him (5)
23 Racecourse slightly rearranged for apprentice (7)
24 African country: it gets about in time (7)
25 Receive unusual command not to obstruct (3,3,2,3,3)

Down

1 Reproach incurred by wayward scholar on Lawrence for killing weeds (6,8)
2 Bird may be true after crude love's resurrected (7)
3 Robin meets Howard at dawn (9)
4 Rise of self-service food — tongue (7)
5 Bend ahead? (7)
6 Remain with model in bath (5)
7 My freedom is essential: I melt otherwise on top (3,2,2)
8 Give two, perhaps, often excepted (7,7)
14 River accompanying straight (9)
16 Fireplace? No thanks! (7)
17 One tear about 5 after a breathing space? (3,4)
18 Felt shy about object of knowledge recommended at Delphi (7)
19 Fish eggs, say, take some hoeing (4,3)
21 Fast nothing! (5)

9

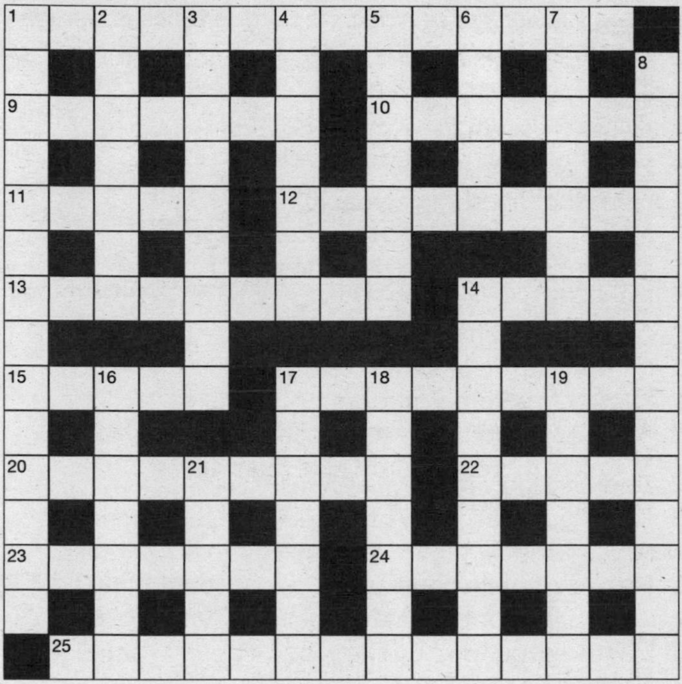

All across solutions have a definite portion which is disregarded in the subordinate part of the clue.

Across

4 Capital little solution (6)
6 Smell of a cyst (8)
9 Household god in a sweat (6)
10 Naval base unhappy about front page (8)
11 In Surrey a fool is king and boss (11)
15 Basically a painting (2,5)
17 Cry's out for time, perhaps (7)
18 Immortelle, unknown possibly near Mamma (11)
22 Heavenly before a student (8)
23 Alternatives for alternative people (6)
24 Magic herb's about right, like Mamma (8)
25 Essay, slightly relative (6)

Down

1 Involve me with hens ... (6)
2 ... put your foot on them first, railwayman (10)
3 Heath surrounded by Dennis (we hear) in anger (8)
4 Nothing opaque? (3,5)
5 Bosh! That could be ablutions taken 3 (3,5)
7 Frank address to swan (4)
8 Assistant gets the wrong idea (4)
12 Clue to Elba shouldn't be kept (10)
13 Accommodation in the dictionary? (8)
14 Ripe moss product repeated by sceptics (8)
16 Battlecry from Marseaux (that's wrong!) (3,5)
19 Jerky characteristic of film maker? (6)
20 Light timber (4)
21 Note of a girl (4)

10

Across

1,5 A certain form of sail is in fashion ... (8,6)
9 ... and a beast right on a holy 5 girl is by ... (8)
10,12,13 ... writer for girls and boys: Bobby's missing about one among us at unfinished service (6,5,9)
14 Summary of "The Return of the Native" makes me change book (4,4,4)
18 Principal prince gets a long way with ropes to pull (4,8)
21 Eccentric, with start for finish, reveals modesty and quiet (9)
23 A man of means? (5)
24 Like a man from Ireland in base (6)
25 One prepared for battle, say — recruit? (8)
26,19 13's Rocket? Jolly d.! (misspelt) (6,6)
27 Stack supports where good person goes bad? (8)

Down

1 Divert pink trout? (6)
2 Finishes portion of paste with U-turn (4,2)
3 Did not lie formerly at canal port so awfully hot (4,5)
4 Rows at length in China, with a stink like Hamlet's uncle's offence? (4,8)
6 Held forth in wheel (5)
7 A form of loathing (8)
8 Offspring raised without shelter make 16 relations (8)
11 Try leaving a Midland town that's going up, then leave old test site (6,6)
15 Snatched by 13, child went to sleep (9)
16 Monkey went abroad and got better (8)
17 Its choir could be of significance in the past (8)
19 See 26
20 Underline relation of illness? (6)
22 Little room for love with strings (5)

11

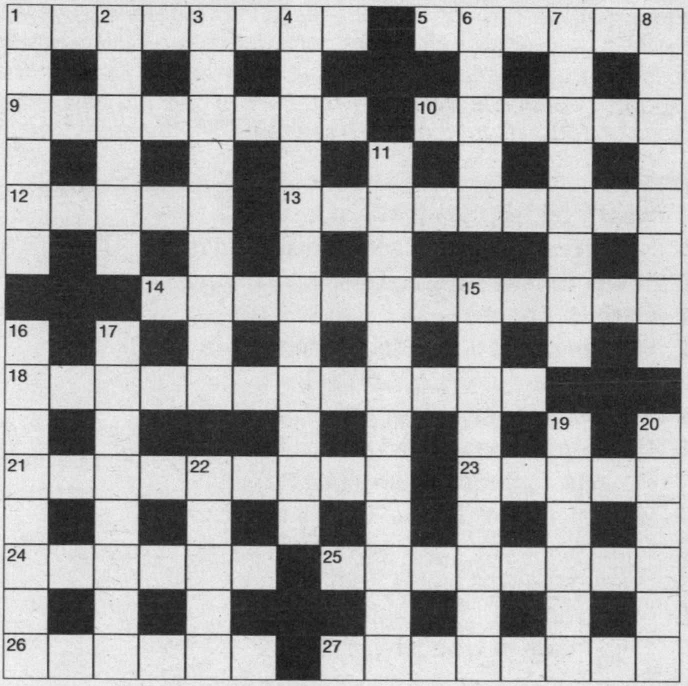

There is a misprint of one letter in each down clue, always in the definition part. Across clues are normal, but in each across solution one letter must be misprinted before entry in the diagram: the misprinted version is always a proper word and the new letter can always be found from the down solutions.

Across

1 Nearly fall, as they that run fast (7)
5 State one's belief as senior academics do? (7)
10 Tower for storing soil, possibly (4)
11 Certainty of being found guilty (10)
12 Roman priest flourished at end of prayer (6)
13 Moll's place infers country (8)
14 Pupil's bitter sweet (9)
16 Century and year easily taken from baby (5)
17 Put him in church to ring bells (5)
19 26 reptile providing he was pink (4,5)
23 First member's right: work with Queen is wrong (8)
24 Seat in the wild North East (6)
26 Inflate an air bubble like a fan (10)
27 Ship made of wood in bay (4)
28 Stop something put on for the publicity? (7)
29 Little mark of wound that's red (7)

Down

2 Novelist cut short by slur (7)
3 New work district for Eleanor 10 (5)
4 Tease prisoner — people's about (7)
6 Marsh grass: it is to revive again (2-4)
7 Deserved to be removed from circulation (9)
8 Scottish touch of gold, right in width (7)
9 Sport before leaving, ere hand or foot goes astray (3,3,3,4)
15 Royal report could be miserly, for example (4,5)
18 Rose is a talker (7)
20 Pick person to be a good waiter (7)
21 End of carriage company with drive going wrong (7)
22 Lack of volcanic matter rising from Arthur's testing place (6)
25 Addition that is counted (5)

12

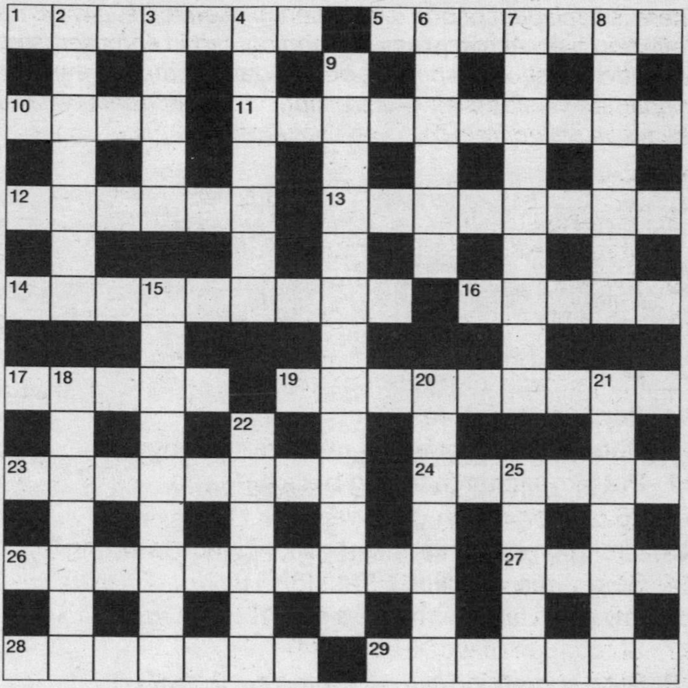

This was puzzle No. 20,000, published on April 11 1994. To mark the occasion, Araucaria pressed a distinguished compiler of competitive verse into what appears to have been somewhat arduous service. Each line includes the usual elements of a clue to the solutions indicated.

Daughter of Zeus! Crazed piner after dullness, **6dn** (10)
  I slept; but press me hard, my forehead smite! **8ac** (8)
Veiled in eternity, yours is the fullness **14ac** (8)
  Of inspiration, given to watch at night. **24ac** (4)
My mind's confused; my object? Get it clear; **17ac** (7)
  And with that one desire, say you've concurred! **21dn** (6)
Dreariness in this hymn let no man hear **25ac** (2,4)
  But see in poetry my thoughts transferred. **15ac** (7)
What cryptic image do I meditate? **10ac** (4)
  From stony ground sprang a perennial flower. **26ac** (8)
In nakedness? Hardly! but grid-confined; **9ac** (6)
  Not strong in growth till raised by student power. **4dn** (7)
  There I (ah, even muddled I) found bliss; **3dn** (6)
  My vow was made — then aid me, Muse, in this! **16dn** (2,4,2)

Fear grips my twisted hair ... to take (some task!) **23ac** (10)
  A hand in this great tale (and — there's the rub — **1dn** (8)
To gain respect) for one wise "ghost" I ask: **19dn** (7)
  Ravisher Muse, this stumbling actor dub! **5dn** (8)
Help an historian ape the Bard; employ **12ac** (6)
  Some poet's wand (a pen?), from Avon's rushes **2dn** (4)
Ink flowing wine-like with loquacious joy. **7dn** (6)
  (Strip vine, squash fruit — we drink what pressure
    crushes!) **11ac** (10)
But TWENTY-THOUSANDTH! I draw back and guard **24dn** (4)
  My speech, buy time, discuss my craft, appeal — **20ac** (4,4)
Barter weak froth for words, and find it hard. **13dn** (10)
  Yet sloth's worst sins zeal stirs — so stir my zeal! **18dn** (8)
  Fair wind, transport, calm-voiced, this ode of mine, **22ac** (6)
  So through degrees I'll reach the bottom line. **22dn** (6)

Mary Holtby

13

Across

1,6 Dreamtime, as opposed to the 19 across 20? (9,5)
9 Here's the complete commercial (5)
10 What the pendulum did, the southwest 'aving been reluctant (5,4)
11 Crazy at keeping the real ale people back on the road (10)
12,14,15 Direction from the 19 across 20 formed party beside bureaux (4,7,2,1,4)
17 Take forty winks outside the insects' home (3,4)
19,20 Gain time at first for drink and play (7,4)
22 Basis for life of senior student, as during concert (10)
25 Driver-drinker losing head and, maybe, perch (5,4)
26 Cake may have some magic ingredient (5)
27 Seaside character (5)
28 Subject of 12 14 15 taking (king having gone mad!) responsibility (for 18) (9)

Down

1 Manet's work was no accident (5)
2 Leave leaver under Monty (6,3)
3 Manure used carelessly without restraint (10)
4 Bad name surrounds leading actor, a keen type (7)
5 Stage words to audience repent of wounding remark (7)
6,24 Old Portuguese colony in scene of mutiny, a place that's out of bounds (2,2,4)
7 Semi-glaucous unknown plant (sea milkwort) (5)
8 Alternate seat — trunk a possibility (4,5)
13 Mother, early in the year, is a motivating influence (10)
14 Given a coat that's tight? (9)
16 Drawing of building on hill? (9)
18 Pirated edition of the 19 across 20 (7)
19 Warning to spectators at match? (5,2)
21 The same either way? (5)
23 The astrologer of Famagusta (5)
24 See 6

14

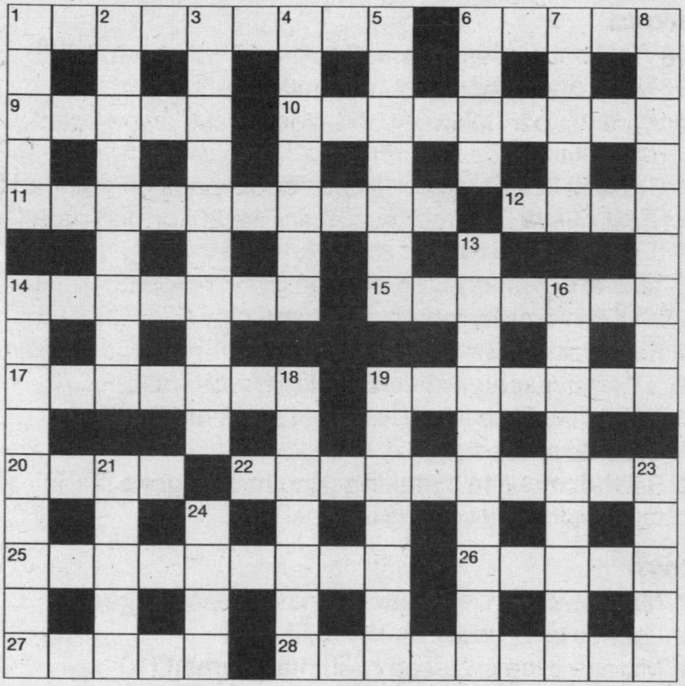

Across

8 Western doctor comes in to pry at sign of spring (8)
9 New term, alternative to "minor earthquake" (6)
10 A lot of detectives are sarcastic (4)
11 Detective story writer from colony (Aden) (5,5)
12 Detective story writer 15 completely missing Sir Bernard (6)
14 Cathedral city to burn (very French) (8)
15 Girl to get nearly wed outside (7)
17 Detective story writer split some cloth (7)
20 First and/or last quarter? (4-4)
22 Detective story writer on southern rock (6)
23 Sadly Graham is no detective story writer (5,5)
24 Detective in need of licence (4)
25 Island between rivers, backing to detective ... (6)
26 ... story writer coining it — riches (8)

Down

1 On entering Canada, tumbled into the snake (8)
2 Due to love, married (4)
3 Doctor's bill to Queen has little weight (6)
4 Terrible panic shrouded in silence: it's greatly reduced (7)
5 Single person in the theatre in the distant past (5,3)
6 Answer takes in Golden Boy, or so we have heard (10)
7 Spooner's detective story writer's dog's called Wilkins (6)
13 Funny fellow, he and his girl need pressure cabins (4-6)
16 Cohabitant's opportunity to marry? (8)
18 Librarian poet around Rhode island hooligan in Australia (8)
19 Strip of cassock? Mythical bird's in awful funk (7)
21 An abbreviated county, English in origin (6)
22 Round field (6)
24 Going for 0 or 100 mph? (4)

15

Each across solution contains a drink, which is disregarded in the subsidiary part of the clue.

Across

7 Max's book meets some resistance (8)
9 In the manner of a warning (6)
10 Unknown emperor (4)
11 He wrote songs to the cabbage (4,6)
12 Fabric for student at home (6)
14 Conservative request to hold one's liquor (4-4)
15 Very large pound of bone (6)
17 Concerned with information (6)
20 Countryman taking the 6.50? (8)
22 Soldier's award for flexible filler (6)
23 Work at eating insect without taking it seriously? (10)
24 Nothing is impossible (2,2)
25 Musket for young lady (6)
26 Like the wild oat, born at hilly city (3,5)

Down

1 Having money, whence springs agitation? (4-2-2)
2 Vital point of Southern stars (4)
3 Bird goes to jail without turn (6)
4 Conserve glass, oriental, for sedan chair bearer (8)
5 Island with a hundred bills is unpredictable (10)
6 Refined in clothing by force (6)
8 A rule in a road in Africa (6)
13 Greedy children of whom five behaved variously (6,4)
16 It's not out of the question for agricultural land to accept some guano (8)
18 What's it lacking in bulk on high? (8)
19 Parmesan implement sounds more famous (6)
21 Home help embracing student is like marquetry (6)
22 Month on border causing chaos (6)
24 Emperor in one room (4)

16

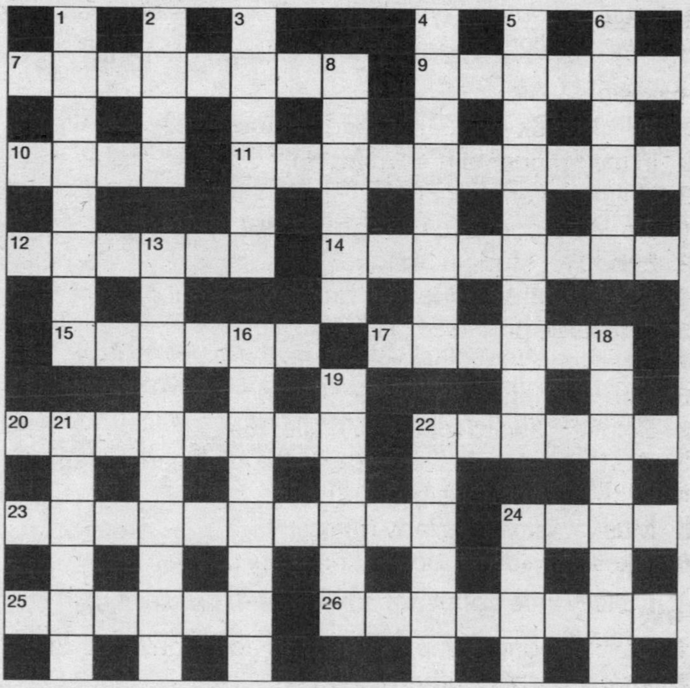

Across

1,4 Ancient patriarch in rash development by fiery chariot racer? (6,8)
9 Almost get cold and a big shock on the Lizard (5)
10 Pushchair, a pet project with an infestation (4,5)
11 Woodwork at the fish gate? (9)
12 A month in Spain is a nuisance (5)
13 Talk books? (5,7)
17 Consequences etc of Prague morals (7,5)
20 Beast expressed satisfaction about craving (5)
21 Schism from church during working period? (9)
23 American writer backed in to knock down our leaders (3,6)
24 Author of "Reflections of a Governess"? (5)
25 Under 50% being under 18 (8)
26 Big gun at billiards (6)

Down

1 Called once about firms at great expense (4,4)
2 One who makes notes with pipe (8)
3 Free love comes in to be parted from (5)
5 English colony confused with suburb? That's all right then (4,4,5)
6 Composer of "The Martyred Mountain"? (5,4)
7 Adriatic merchantman strikes a hopeful note inside (6)
8 Saw the negative principle in loss of tension (6)
10 Hell of a clue for Pi (10,3)
14 Marsupial, a stunner, in the fashion of a carnivore (5,4)
15 Part I in a short day has "a grievous fault" (8)
16 A boy to call up male voice choir in unison? (2,3,3)
18 Non-vocal beat? (6)
19 Dredge the River Swan? (6)
22 Fishy drawing of 10 down in water (5)

17

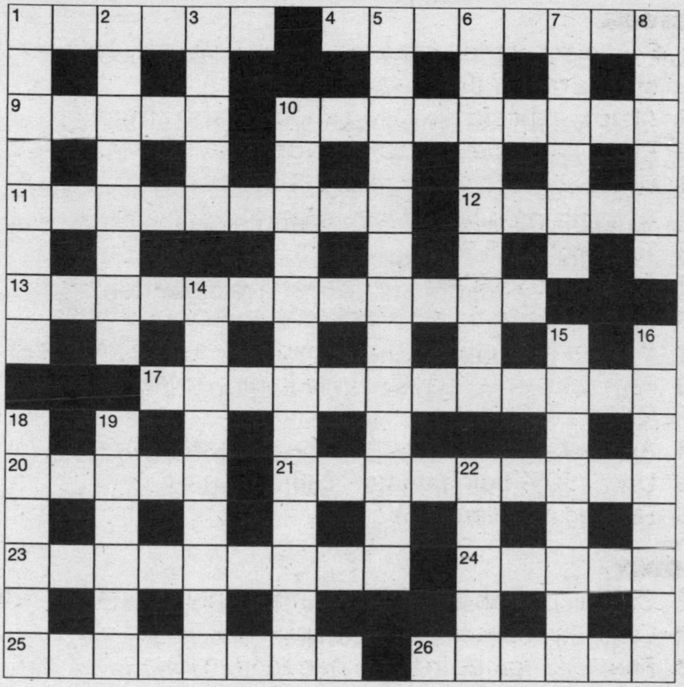

Across

1 Not married for money in a European arrangement? (6,8)
9 Stay in the air for Barrie's utopia (5,4)
10,11 Poet whose utterances are of value (10)
12 False or true – can he tell? (9)
13 True – cannot otherwise take in saint (8)
14 It makes me sick when they quote me the wrong way (6)
17 Stick for a curtain? (6)
19 Place for spectators no longer available: don't get involved (5,3)
22 Expose fraudulent scheme coming out in print? (3,6)
24 Part of such reactionary paintings in Sanskrit book (5)
25 See 6
26 Nursemaid accepting a tribute from leading cleric (9)
27 Struggle for generation of witty Harry's ear, possibly (6,5,3)

Down

1 Cinque port theatre showing "The Go-between"? (8-6)
2 Stew up front with rainstorm to follow (7)
3 Protector for Jewish quarter, rather slow moving (9)
4 Cross about resistance: it's rough work (8)
5 Contract in connection with Italian leader (6)
6,25 Unfinished work by journalist; a blow to the area (5,5)
7 Despicable character with tear flowing (7)
8 Productive enterprise: East German lady goes about finding a large plume (7,7)
15 Awfully frumious little name for a root of ... (5,4)
16 In the theatre it's always the cheapest section (8)
18 Tycoon's right to swindle: there's a lot of it about (7)
20 Striking cry of alarm raised at plughole? (7)
21 Monastic rule prescribes degree in easy subject: on your head be it (6)
23 Less than foreign articles (5)

18

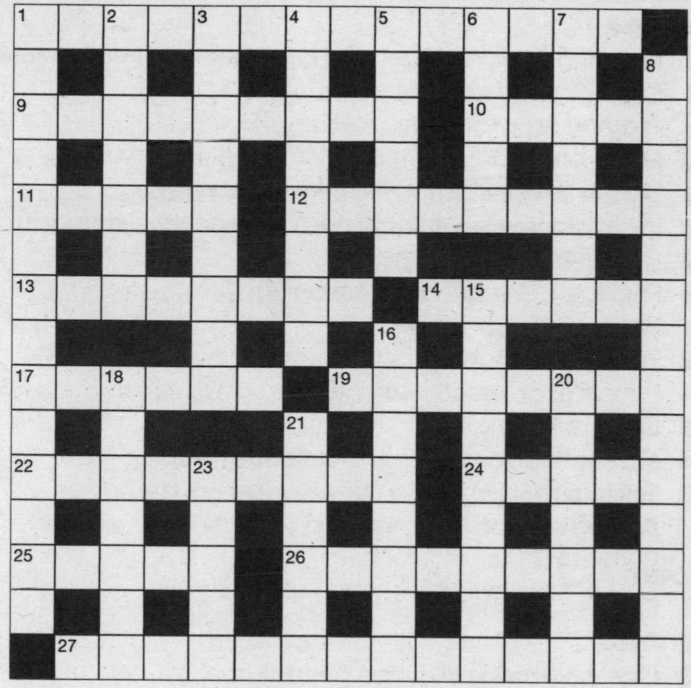

Across

1 Greeting from Wooster who has eaten his headgear (4,2)
4 Larger than life sort of verse? (6)
9 A grand spot for a mausoleum (4)
10 Order changed! Company! Left face! Fire! (4,6)
11 Backward lot in a hostile spirit (6)
12 What did you say about seed? Any day in January (8)
13 Bushy-tailed lunatic twigs (9)
15 Duplicate drops in the kitchen (4)
16 Story of a book for bed (4)
17 Tails give new image to Tracey, possibly (9)
21 Laughter at needlework? (8)
22 Eat or talk turkey? (6)
24 Tip: Borstal may be what he needs (6,4)
25 Tell to surrender (4)
26 Having no word processor, do it again in its entirety, perhaps (2-4)
27 One of the cast who knows his lines? (6)

Down

1 One who drives West's a dead duck (7)
2 Warning of a wing man's opening (5)
3 Trite saying for metal worker (7)
5 The object of batting is to cover the ball (6)
6 How one drives, of course, not 8 (3,3,3)
7 Chanel, a crazy person, may get shy (7)
8 Custom-built from French book, to a certain degree coming first (4,2,7)
14 Select few lacking, inclination? (5,4)
16,20 Substantiate, accomodate, or incarcerate (3,2,2,4,2)
18 Constrain a giant, say? (7)
19 Nothing left of blanket? (3,4)
20 See 16
23 Roll round — take the railway (5)

19

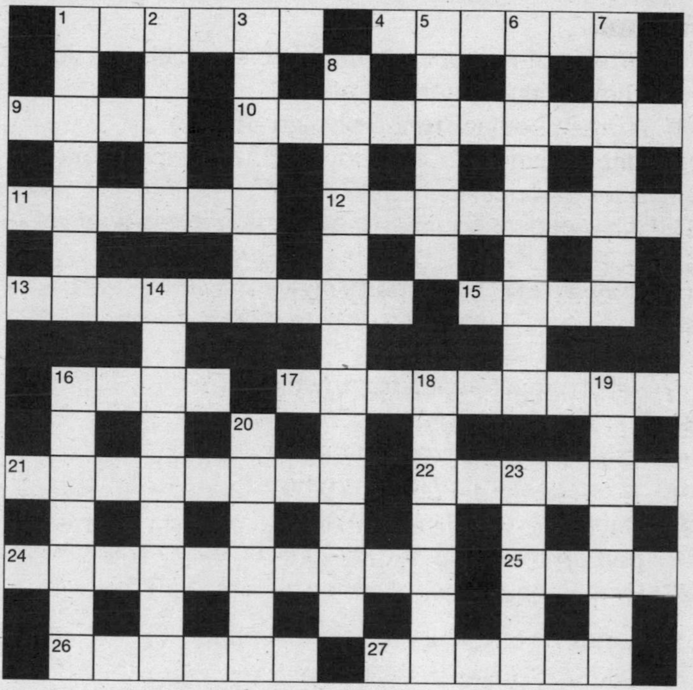

Across

1 Show some proof it will harm us — I challenge you (5,4)
6 Where to find 1d, like 1a (4)
10 It takes one back to the ancient poet (5)
11 Milton's work about power and law in an intricate system (9)
12 Class leaders come in to avail themselves again of a hermit (7)
13 Stuffy and far from 'irsute? (7)
14,17 Sherriff's work in a date to stop my mistress roaming? (8,3,2,6,7)
21 Full of angst (French for anything) (7)
22 Routine version of the foetal position (2,5)
24 Build up to two hundred turns incorrectly (9)
25 Star of the Virgin, Southern type (5)
26 In and out sort of season? (4)
27 Mad Hatter and God may be played tantalisingly (4,2,3)

Down

1 A drink an amateur sent up to a prince (8)
2 Rising French writer's tree (5)
3 Victim can argue another way to get round (14)
4 Tell occupation in "going for gold"? (7)
5 Hit the hay, perhaps, at shearers' feast (4-3)
7 Mathematically, ten pixies make just over fifty (7,2)
8 A fool it's crazy to help (6)
9 French poet led RAF astray with five hundred birds on TV, perhaps (6,2,6)
15 A French play to end sadly, deprogrammed to become … (9)
16 … unaware of topless Italian social worker (8)
18 Make further contact with TUC hero? (7)
19 Man without love having taken more water? (7)
20 Remnant of a stroke on the right side of the wicket (6)
23 The east side of Southfork (5)

20

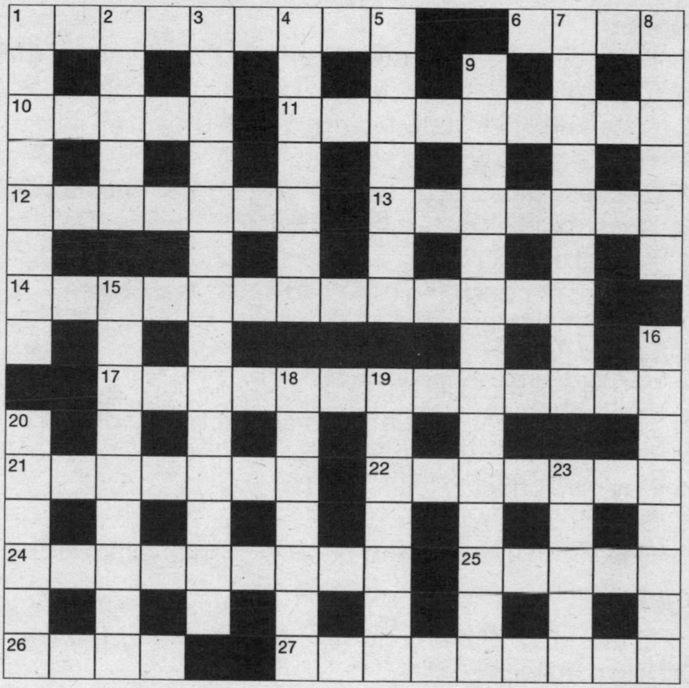

Across

1 Settle down — Mummy's seen it — I'll protect you (6,6)
8 China gives audience to Burns' men, then Steinbeck's (7)
9 A starting point in divinity, with a little beard (7)
11 Friend in love with African capital (7)
12 22 causing mishap, perhaps, among little children (3,4)
13 Nous sommes ensemble, in part (5)
14 Mutual objects of one in reflection and the king (4,5)
16,25 Copper pursuing rude bird during walk takes freedom fighter food (9,7)
19 Lady without 13 turned mother (5)
21 The tale of the Bill? (7)
23 He propounded a creative force with lumps of ice attached (7)
24 Day revolutionary left a bag (7)
25 See 16
26 Rose up in a rage about publicity being absurd (12)

Down

1 One and a half diamonds in old the tyrant of 11 (3,4)
2 Slip road with post (7)
3 Nothing about one holding a standard — there's nothing like it (9)
4 The jolly 13? (5)
5 Capital cleaner for a politician — go away without … (7)
6 … accidentally causing tears to English trees? (7)
7 Skim — one glass will do — sent out from conclave? (5,7)
10 Unfairly choose record at speed, about one a minute (12)
15 Member in message that can be scaled (9)
17 Scale of movement for prosperous piece of land (7)
18 Revise with a wash? (5,2)
19 Dance company following customs (7)
20 Field event with pole — talk about it (7)
22 Scene of revelry for Scrabble players? (5)

21

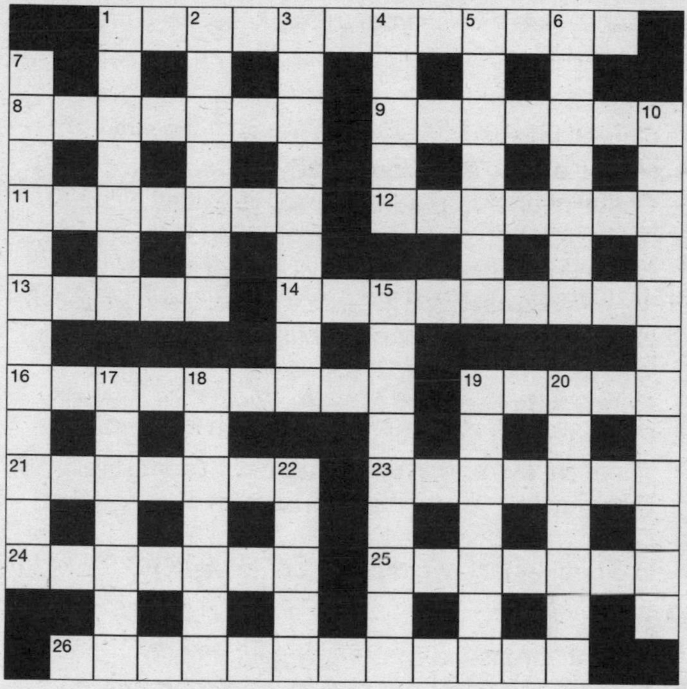

Only G and Q are missing from the alphabetical pattern of the solutions.

Across

1 Church job for sailor, C-in-C (partly), say? (6)
4 Pay 18 across about one ready to listen? Not so (6)
9 Castle offerin' ... pig with no tail in a stew (2,5,2,6)
10 Military transport docked, containing local spirit (6)
11 Coin used in composition by Ludwig and Leo (8)
12 My name is changed in Lincolnshire: it's in Devon (8)
14 Number — 100 replacing its first — for judging to (6)
15 Was sick with love, as it's said (6)
18 Honours that are paid (8)
21 Fruit at cape has quality of sin (8)
22 There are five and a half or more with some Welsh (6)
24 One way to X-ray a small house with porridge (15)
25 Gives in returns (6)
26 Old beer — last two digits incomplete (6)

Down

1 A night abroad interrupts any payment (7)
2 A knight of King Arthur makes some harmony (5)
3 French writer with miserable children (7)
5 Jacob sheep abandoned by lady with beer mug (7)
6 Arbitrator upset by new client with spot on skin (9)
7 Think of glasswork? (7)
8 Something to hang on a hot pipe (6)
13 Figure of fantasy in more fabulous beast (9)
16 Good food sent up by rail from sty (7)
17 What's straight and not simple? A conservative (3-4)
18 Critic of classical country cousins? (6)
19 Navy's upset about soldier raised as jurist (7)
20 Enlighten your classmate with some telemessage, say? (4,3)
23 Cape with grapes (5)

22

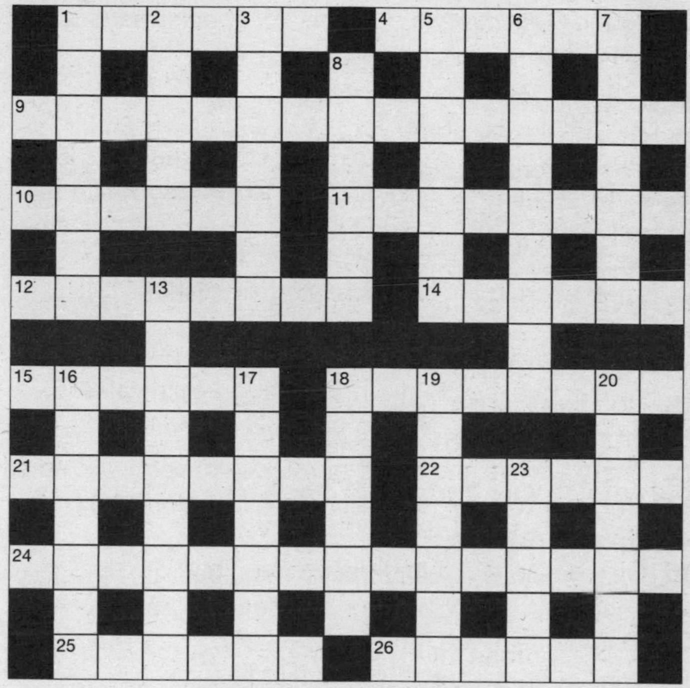

Across

7 Return some work to bogus law man (7)
8 A lot of blood in grey pope (7)
10 Cut out of a region (6)
11 Impediment with a capital I following employee (8)
12,22 Defile currency just enough to get through (4,4)
13 Duties can't produce holiness (10)
14 Place spy round the English royal family (11)
19 Suffer each to produce warmed-up dishes (10)
22 See 12
23 Like an Italian city without a Spanish provincial (8)
24 Front of bus, hesitantly, has an aggregate value (6)
25 Scots freak has power to get LSD experience: hypocrosy's epitaph! (7)
26 I am in to your friend of St Paul's (7)

Down

1 Cloth provides naval drink for male beast (7)
2 Being wedded to the cause of seal soup? (8)
3 Documents of the fourth estate? (6)
4 Beast about to catch the dark lady (8)
5 It goes off a selfish man (6)
6 Golden country round in Arden? (7)
9 MP from Ireland, by hap Sinn Fein, colleague of Mr 7, 14 duke of 24, Lord 25, Sir 6 18, Sir 8 1, and Sir 26 17 (7,4)
15 Nervous pain — I nurse it badly (8)
16 Men do not change in London (8)
17 Busybodies are increasing in polish (7)
18 Doctor has a duty in water shortage (7)
20 Habitats — also of huncles? (6)
21 Unmoved in Bristol, I dare say (6)

23

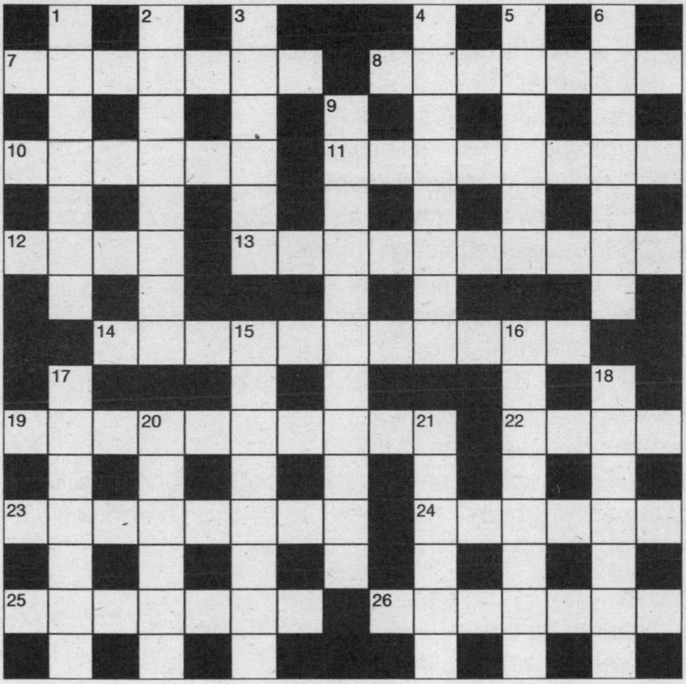

Across

1 Die of excitement and final responsibility for space traveller (4,3,6)
10 Symbol that 'inders itself (9)
11 Ship reaches pole using gas (5)
12 City is ahead of the audience (5)
13,14 Motorway junction has the Guardian back on film (9,7)
16 Church leader quiet on quarrel (7)
18 Boy upset by semirepulsive beetle (7)
20 Like a couple of Scots between left and right — would it had been! (4,3)
21 Fly round 16 with a runner on the box (4,5)
23 Noisy enchantress ? (5)
24 Deer to dash its head (5)
25 Quantity, sphere and length of bottom of ring (5,4)
26 An artist requires hard work, love and an endless supplier of wine and woman (13)

Down

2 Marked as compiler is by paper's editor (9)
3 Jerome's soldiers defeated by Macbeth (Act I Scene 2) (5)
4 Make harsh sounds "delivered by a drab" (7)
5 Uproar over small coin for nightlight (3,4)
6 Railway junction without end ends without beginning — applaud! (4,5)
7 Number of pieces? (5)
8 Singular gibbet has spectacles for soldiers accompanying 3 (13)
9 Not too well — at home otherwise (13)
15 Improve upon "Member's brother eaten by duck" (9)
17 Wine ready mixed where Wordsworth saw the daffodils (6,3)
19 Exam for bigshot? (5,2)
20 Student who makes a quid? (7)
22 11 was hydrogen with a lot of water in it (5)
23 Undress could be comic (5)

24

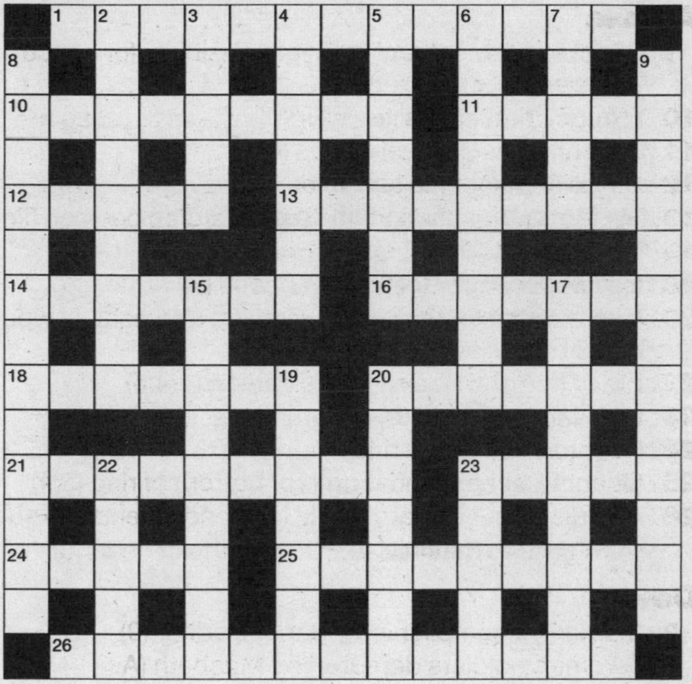

Across

1 Following what I'm saying? (4,2)
4 First prize without trouble? Get on! (4,3)
9 Dickens's first character is Dombey, out to make a ghost? (9)
10 Extended point in a record (5)
11 Lessing, author of 26 28 in colour (5)
12,13 "4 across 10 1 across ______" (26,28) (3,4,2,3,2,2)
15 Corrupt passage? (6)
17 Diverted from sea with mud (6)
19 Saga of prophetic quality, say (7)
22 Lots of hay and honey: that's dandy! (5-4)
24,14 Plantation tale with Columbian scent (5,4,5)
26,28 Poem by Jonson and Pound on tailless beast (5,3,4)
27 Girl from Belize with hat off (9)
28 See 26
29 Witch goes to madhouse with change of heart (6)

Down

1 Fat young spiv? (4,3)
2 Make fool into poet (5)
3 Small time people to us of great importance (9)
4 Note for journalist in Scots alley — it's in Wales (7)
5 Coming for the majority, trouble in Old English (2,3)
6 Please stop, old boy. I've got toothache (9)
7 Postprandial summary? (6)
8 Abhor (see articles) (6)
14 See 24
16 Bad fault with Rome express (9)
18 Sundew for doctor on the big time (7)
19 Stuff for the fabulously rich? Not quite (6)
20 Woman's meat with plum (7)
21 Beetle or Scottish horse? (6)
23 Sound replicas of dog (5)
25 Belief — long dissertation with no beginning (5)

25

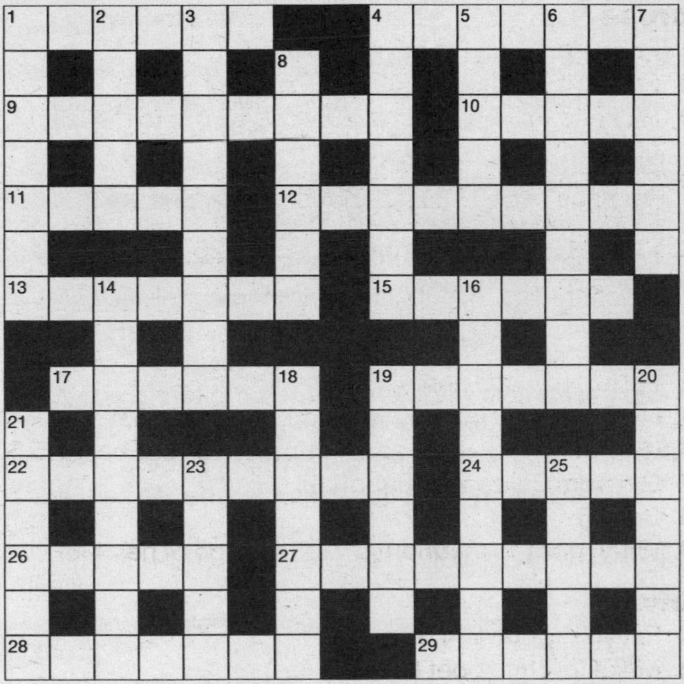

Solve the clues and fit in the solutions where they will go.

A Marine birds can be seen backing a bird that's marine (4)
B Make a very loud hum: Beadle, then heartless ones come (6-4)
C Recreated a storm: conifer, beauteous in form (5,4)
D From the circle I steeled maybe two trains are revealed (6-8)
E To be puzzling's its aim: find variations in game (6)
F Is denoted by L — fit, if the letters may tell (8)
G The descendants here ran daggers on targets to scan (5-5-9)
H Did the carpets without oxygen hung round about (8)
I Is a river, it shows; into the Danube it flows (4)
J Setter's after June's first: one who predicted the worst (6)
K Here the viceroy's the thing: I have what he had, the king (7)
L's in thin plates: mid the dead see the Field-Marshal who fled (8)
M When in further, I act: gold piece in galleon once packed (7)
N East Vietnam's endless mess makes for ingenuousness (7)
O For your salad to grease here is the unction of peace (5-3)
P Steadfast prince finds the queen cutting: it makes vipers green (11)
Q Knightly, selfless, absurd: kiss ring in leave, I see (heard) (8)
R About one in what's gold something elastic is told (10)
S How old's ox? O'er the deep passengers travel so cheap (8)
T — heater's in — doesn't loose long long-winded streams of abuse (7)
U In effect's null and void: person by Kofi employed? (11)
V Just a surface it makes: victory day never breaks (6)
W Cunning idea, breath that one can't fail to hear (6)
X Is for Francis, the saint: vex with an air that is quaint (6)
Y My dear Charlie appears blind to the passage of years! (5,9)
Z In a frenzy methinks alcoholises the drinks (4)

26

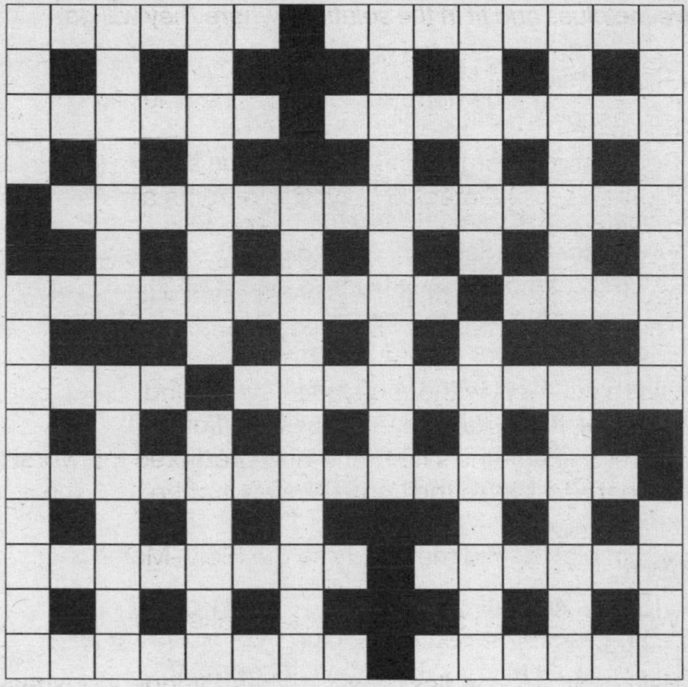

Across

1 Beast and what it did by itself above the stage? (7)
5 Beast's mistake's a bloomer (7)
9 Beast on a plate with branches (5)
10 Beast's skin, or ambush for it: dig here (5,4)
11 Beast, male, with skill of crusading king (4-5)
12 Beast with degree for teaching (5)
13 A looker for a listener? Not far off (5)
15 Watch carriage of destructive insect (6-3)
18 Beast beats salt deposits (4,5)
19 Telling brothers, forbidding many (5)
21 If reversed, reserved and suspicious (5)
23 Beast, one that has a nap, is a destroyer (9)
25,26 Beast lacerates pretended sorrow (9,5)
27 Bird goes round pole with guard (7)
28 Theology should go with philosophy (7)

Down

1 Most of logical consequence in envelope (7)
2 Delay encountered coming up river to spring (9)
3 God gives every satisfaction, it seems (5)
4 A hat-trick may be purifying (9)
5 Outcast acquired accountant first (5)
6 Being short of spirit, he turned down grill (9)
7 In bed? Not true! (5)
8 Snoop around Miss Horne to be complete (7)
14 Flower bush joint (9)
16 One listener may be hard to squash (9)
17 Some French language about hotel with German director (5,4)
18 Something missing! Can't it hear? Can you? (7)
20 Impressionist's witticism about golden islands (7)
22 Beast's trail's not good! (5)
23 Some British and American city at sea (5)
24 Reputed to repeat (5)

27

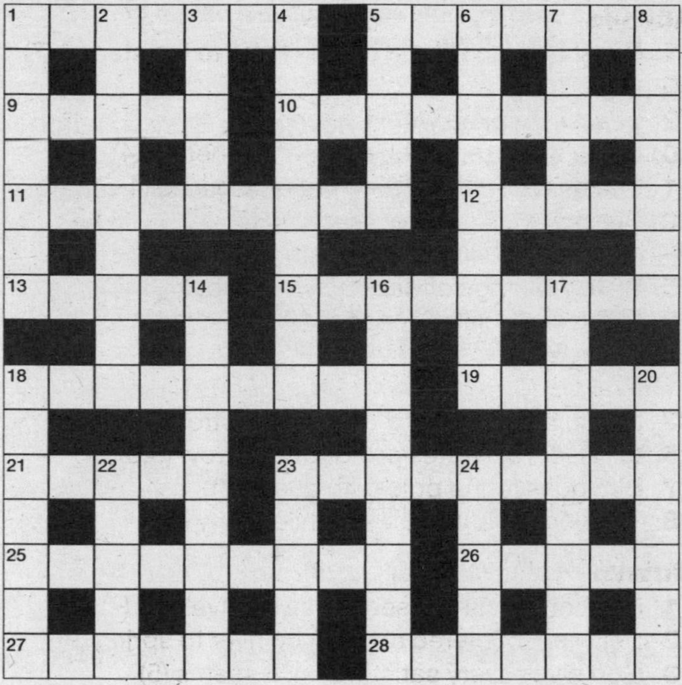

Solutions to each multiple clue contain a part of the body; which has been disregarded in the subsidiary part of the clue.

Across

9 Lightweight prince has backing of a French church (4,5)
10,4 Christian about to speak of Old Master (5,8)
11 Isthmus with connection that goes round and hangs down (7)
12 Begin with a bare church roof? (4,3)
13 See 3
14 Contest a point with false friend in camera (10)
16 One who suffers with his pupil? (7)
17 See 21
19 Sort of tonic within record, one in alphabetical order? (10)
22,26 Made ready to defend (9)
24 A river — a river ebbing — is an unusual treat (7)
25 Defined as having shareholders (7)
26 See 22
27 Extra lot of cream indeed! (9)

Down

1 As food for toaster it's unconvincing — best thing so far (4-6,5)
2 Spot ant gone for antenatal feeding (8)
3,23,13 Queen in nursery school (as it were) on the border (14)
4 See 10
5 See 20
6 They have visions of a table in Roman times (9)
7 Cotswold town developed by the Tudors (6)
8 Bill's debut, not ours, without note before the putting down of a foot? (3,5,7)
15 Dual purpose furniture for one presiding over a county? (5-4)
17 Disused railway in credit, strangely (8)
18 Dead bird resurrected without turning into toothy peg (8)
20,5 Pigment for China dog holding memory plates (6,6)
21,17across Runyon character faked a Tintoret (6,7)
23 See 3

28

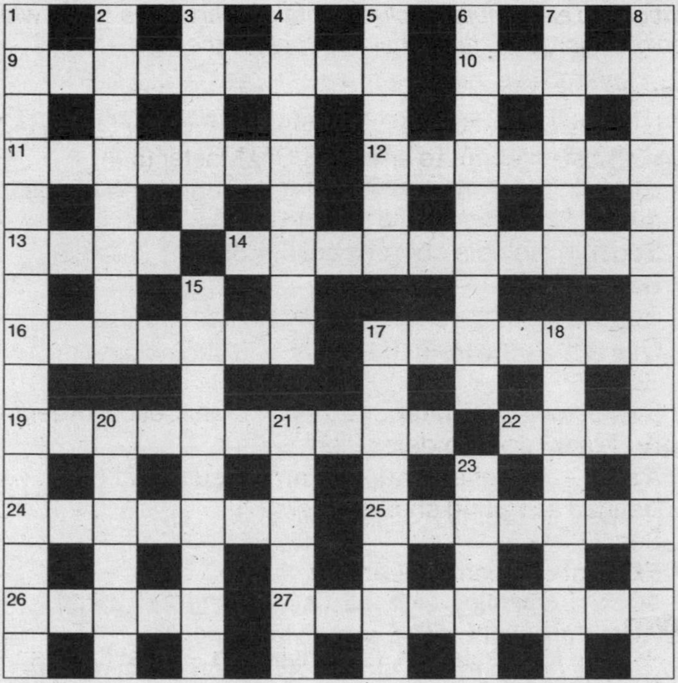

Across

1 Drama preserved? Be cautious (4,4)
5 My robe was made before birth (6)
9 Destructive creatures returning set about holy man (8)
10 Backing 1 down instincts is unwise (6)
11 Surcingle, we hear? (6,8)
14,17,16,23 Literary grand slam? (5,5,2,3,4)
15,16,20 Insoluble geographical problem? (5,2,3,5)
17 See 14
20 See 15
22 Hand the wine from the rocks — it should get you 14 15 16 20 (8,6)
24 Overtake for one mile, 14 15 (6)
25 We shall take the trouble to become rich (4-2-2)
26 Give up Sappers' emblem? (6)
27 Report on top: talk of 1984! (8)

Down

1,13 Starts writing with aunt's pepper pot (4,3,2,5)
2 Settle an island with German leaders (7)
3 Sort of beach that's refreshingly short of characters (7)
4 No charge for Rodin's work (11)
6 Apostle of the West on the carpet (7)
7 Drive back the church from the sepulchre, perhaps (7)
8 Fiddler and son need no introduction (3,7)
12 Cheerio cads! This could be Canterbury! (11)
13 See 1
18 "Brooks no refusal" is in this month's (7)
19 23-maker, a ruler without socialists' backing (7)
20 Gases for cakes? (7)
21 About a hundred fail to shut again (7)
23 See 14

29

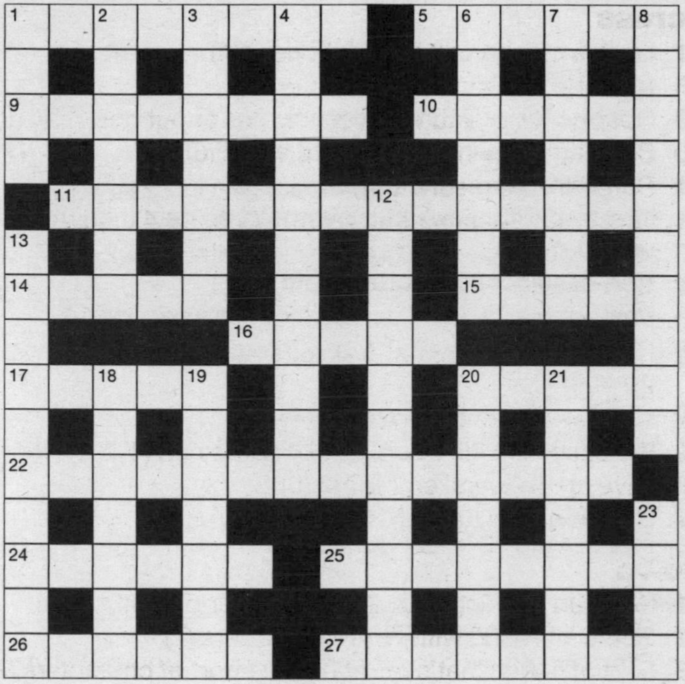

Across

4 Motown (Oxford) poet takes heart from plant of the 19 (6)
6 Not one for a day in the recent past (3,5)
9 Penultimate shaft for plant of the 19 (6)
10 Portable instrument, sequel to drain in 15s (8)
11 Turn and turn anew with overdraft as new though outside? (11)
15 Sort of suit or suet sorted right (7)
17 Plant of the 19, last year's winner, not second (7)
18 Plant of the 19 needs help with curve and small point (6,5)
22 Carob is seaweed to wild boar (8)
23,20 Go astray after champagne and money in South Africa (10)
24 Type of 8 with fruit associated with 19 (8)
25 Plant of the 19 is let out after catch (6)

Down

1 Smith with Bryan's hat? (6)
2 Dramatic passion in clarity endlessly confused (10)
3 Plant of the 19, cut short by Maud, cooked Indian food (8)
4 Squirty cream's top's off — request to stop (3,5)
5 Plant meaning bitterness with evidence of furniture beetle (8)
7 Joints for fruit of ... (4)
8 ... plant got out of bed (4)
12 Plant of the 19, sister and brother to be right? (4,6)
13 Expose the intoxicated hermetic? (8)
14 Inferior (anag?) (3-5)
16 Titans represented by crossword setter in newspaper (8)
19 Rods by roads (6)
20 See 23
21 Go up after 14 (say) with keen expectation (4)

30

Across

1 Drawn by drunkard entertaining glutton? (6)
5 Hang City, defeated in sport (8)
9 Berry before spring in the RAF (8)
10 Discount to be returned in the cost (6)
11 Security precaution leads to quiet air (5,7)
13 A little bit of Sunday (4)
14 Drunkard not at home? (8)
17 Children return without a thing to eat on the threshold (4,4)
18 Not a straight fight (4)
20 Organ and choir, pianissimo! It may be obscene! (12)
23 At heart become a dwarf (6)
24 The monkey travelled and got better (8)
25 Repartee for the Christmas bird? (4,4)
26 Cleopatra's annoyance? (6)

Down

2 Leave transport in public land (4)
3 Father of electricity? (9)
4 Fashionable essay about death? (6)
5 The Beatles' wasn't a gallant ship (6,9)
6 Motor van, one crashed by a learner at a celebration (8)
7 List, on board (5)
8 In No 7 cold cream is evident (10)
12 Surveyor? He's in trouble with a broken tile (10)
15 Vegetable requiring skill: I fail to swallow it! (9)
16 Ticklish business bracketed in Hansard (8)
19 Composer has something to eat at home (6)
21 About to drink up a river (5)
22 Came down the mountain (4)

31

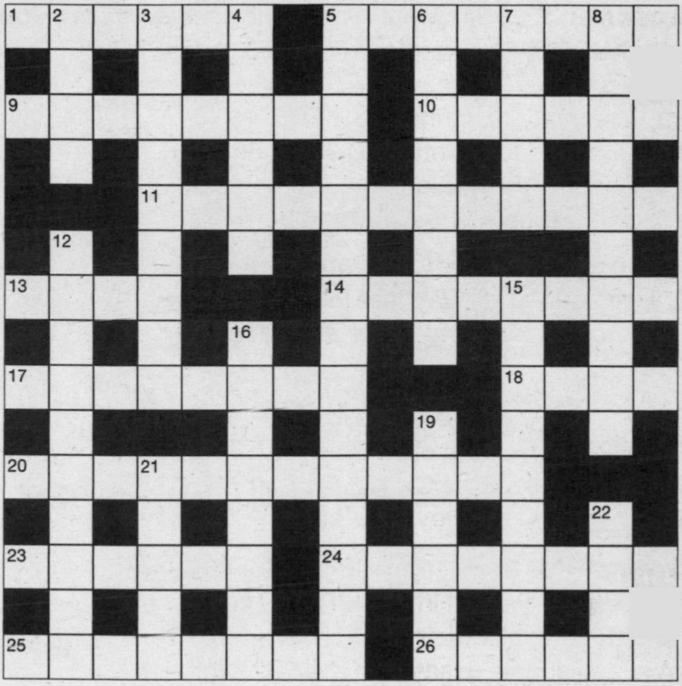

Puzzles Nos. 32 to 35 form a series. The unclued lights belong to a group suggested by 12, 20, 22 and 24.

Across

1 (7)
5 (7)
9 Fireside game (5)
10 (9)
11 Utility art gets nominal status (10)
12 Religious writer, we hear (4)
14 Descents in writing — for ruffled feathers? (11)
18 (5,6)
21 A cat in a scrap (4)
22 Sort of tissue etc, formed to give tacit approval about (10)
25 Peas cooked by fools, the shipping authorities (3,6)
26 (5)
27 Stays at home to prevent wrongdoing (5,2)
28 Don't be afraid to speak, maybe (4,3)

Down

1 Time up, one may suggest (6)
2 (6)
3 Libra translated by snake in gas-holder (3-7)
4 Bill Hill on the boards (5)
5 Bobby Shaftoe's goose with a net inside (4,2,3)
6 Frank has nothing to write (4)
7 Excessive and illicit talking can be explosive (3,5)
8 Antiquity is shrouded in dense gas (8)
13 Rubber cat interrupts Christian after a time (10)
15 (9)
16 (8)
17 (8)
19 Forward girls get six men (6)
20 Woolly cow? (6)
23 Spied a boy turning journalist (5)
24 A service to the crowd (4)

32

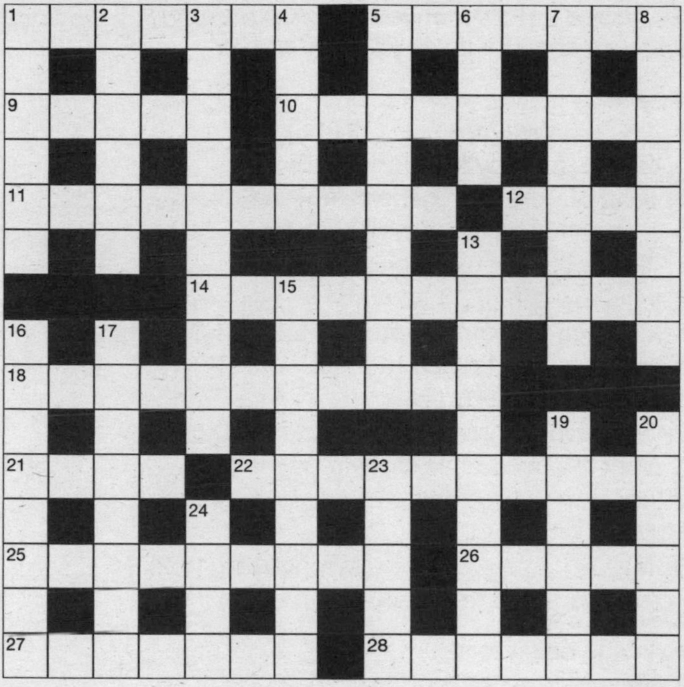

The unclued lights continue the previous puzzle: compare 6 and 12 with No. 32's 20 and 24.

Across

1 "_____ love, not _____!" (4,3)
5 Baby's malady's unfathomable (7)
9 Kind of American general (5)
10 Petronius' half-human image (9)
11 The Latin sort has leanings (6,4)
12 (4)
14 Baal, go and quaff water for Israel (4,2,5)
18 In pious glee I'd had the last word (11)
21 Storm in tragedy (4)
22 Star turn in a chap that's austere (10)
25 Vary the beat as potency requires (9)
26 (5)
27 (7)
28 (7)

Down

1 Flying collector (6)
2 (6)
3 (10)
4 Trees to be put in another place (5)
5 In which choirs are responsive on hatpins? (9)
6 (4)
7 (8)
8 Marginal decider at football (8)
13 A new island for an old protestant (10)
15 (9)
16 (8)
17 (8)
19 (6)
20 Maestro! Maestro! It's thickly spread within (6)
23 In spirit he speaks of cold rhubarb (5)
24 (4)

33

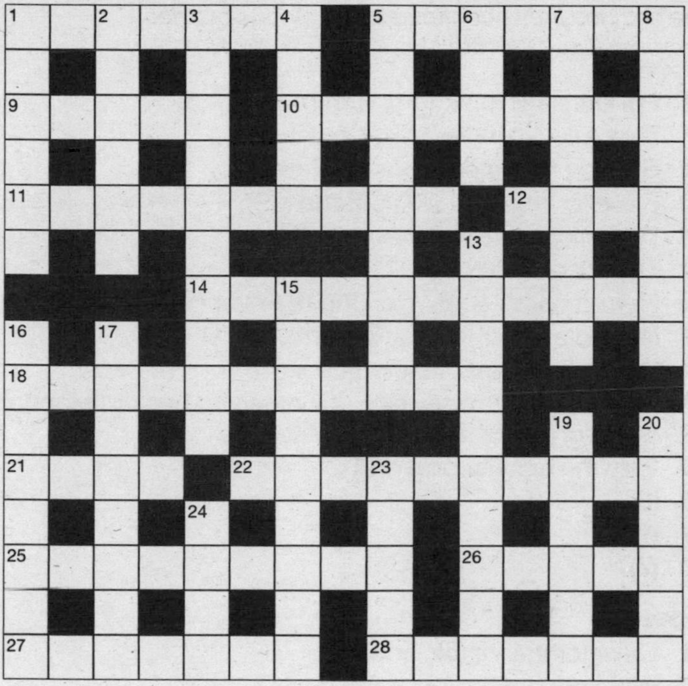

See the two previous puzzles.

Across

1 For drinking to Victory, turn purple (4,3)
5 I am a cur to write in French (7)
9 Stout, with other things, is deadly (5)
10 Reveller was misspelt seaman (9)
11 Diabolical clue in fair puzzle (10)
12 Dye for a cipher (4)
14 Return home, rowing round the river (11)
18 Picked around in Iona with views (11)
21 Possibly sinless Russian bear (4)
22 "The ________s they say … Come you back to Mandalay (Kipling) (6-4)
25 Painting or sweeping? (9)
26 (5)
27 (7)
28 (7)

Down

1 Cake for the loquacious? (6)
2 Warning: don't skate here! (6)
3 (10)
4 Might the queen take a prisoner? (5)
5 Obscurity — anything badly put across (9)
6 (4)
7 (8)
8 (8)
13 My dear, dear wandering woolgatherer (10)
15 (9)
16 (8)
17 (8)
19 (6)
20 Customer gets 51% (6)
23 Russian town, a knockout in a bus (5)
24 (4)

34

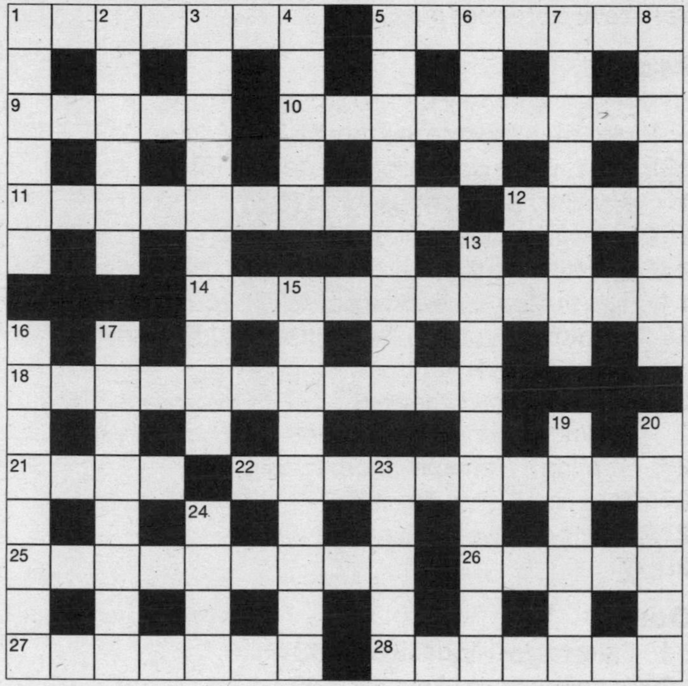

See the three previous puzzles.

Across

1 (7)
5 Radio man most of the day played cricket (7)
9 Stout English get decorations (5)
10 Parnellite head of household (4-5)
11 Piety without love is excellence (10)
12 Opposition to the Youth Leader (4)
14 Break the ice, a pastime causing bad blood (11)
18 "Twilight and ______, and after that the dark" (Tennyson) (7,4)
21 Bit back the catch (4)
22 Absolute minimum – and certainly not (5,2,3)
25 Letter from a chap with personality (9)
26 Idle, unintelligible drops (5)
27 Was productive but gave up (7)
28 (7)

Down

1 Injustices for King George's Own (6)
2 (6)
3 Inside a list I can be impractical (10)
4 Unpaid soldier in Eden's second river (5)
5 (9)
6,24 (8)
7 (8)
8 Red rising when it's light early in June (5,3)
13 Log 1 turns into Fidel, the alchemist (10)
15 Coloured swineherds on the Heath (9)
16 (8)
17 (8)
19 (6)
20 (6)
23 Part of letter backfires (5)
24 See 6

35

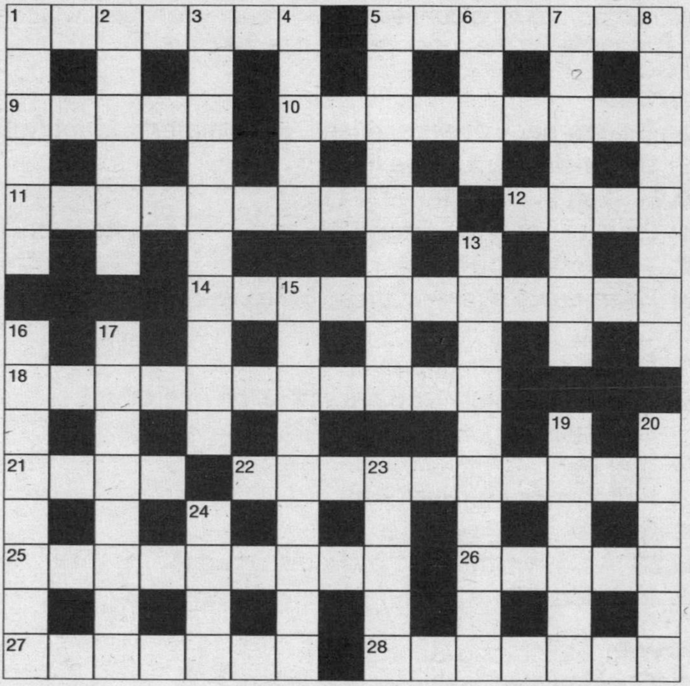

Each across solution contains one of four residences, which is disregarded in the subsidiary part of the clue.

Across

8 Quarter back priest's objectively immaterial identity (8)
9 Unsubstantial, I agree (6)
10,24 Left blade in Texas? (4,4)
11 Revolutionary stomachs return of fenny snake (5,5)
12 Was first called (6)
14 Sines curve? Very much so (when wearing a suit?) (2,6)
15 See 20
17 Prophet's place of prayer? (7)
20,15 Mum in No. 1 tailback where the Intercity stops (4,4,7)
22 See 25
23 Plumber, not so thin (10)
24 See 10
25,22 Mud in rotten tree by Roman road (6,6)
26 Irresponsible adventure — cease trading (8)

Down

1 Cooking the roast affects resistance (8)
2 Barrie's pirate saying who he is? (4)
3 Long ago counselled poor Davies (till black in the face?) (6)
4 No chemicals wanted in cargo? (7)
5 I'm a spy, so change conferences (8)
6 Bad lad in shelter from tough jobs in prison (4,6)
7 Goddess of 19 26 (6)
13 Job of classical professor at a distance in study (5,5)
16 Frank holds dim upper-class characters in drug scene (5,3)
18 Green stones for red males (8)
19 It's unchristian to put the bird on the fire (7)
21 Sheltered in the British manner (or rather the French) (1,5)
22 Tidy tree (6)
24 Enclosure for a month (4)

36

Across

7 Boy or girl? Boy (Scots) and Cypriot leaders show courage (8)
9 Having no qualification, escaped into painting (6)
10 See 2
11 Increase of elastic on a twist (10)
12 South of France, a bed out of the shade (6)
14 Greek achieved a rich tan (8)
15 Don't leave boy around river (4,2)
17 Consented to a vice (6)
20 Revolutionary without work on Tuesday first married beggar (8)
22 Notes in bottles (6)
23 Riverside parking without charge at half-size store (4-6)
24 Seat without 24 down on 24 down (4)
25 Customer put the East in Eastwood (6)
26 Scandalised by disorganised tour for senior citizens? (8)

Down

1 Flags of Pennsylvania, 6, not the enemy's (8)
2,10 Economist and postman in capital rhyme (4,4)
3 Trouble for posh home around river (6)
4 Cruelly tease confounded paper (8)
5 Crazy architect without aspiration, joining Navy, gets the bird (6,4)
6 An attempt by artist at 24 across (6)
8 Act shy, displaying craft (6)
13 One that skips a page describing a cockroach? (4-6)
16 Stop up, stubbornly refusing to exchange a similar letter (8)
18 Month always keeps one as man always was in Much Ado (8)
19 Strip without a raised decoration: it's a point of view (6)
21 Too true about student pursuing love (6)
22 Shot, about to corrode, must be compact (6)
24 Cape for runner (4)

37

Across

1 Do a bit of housework that isn't productive (4,4)
5 Hang the horses! (6)
9 French soldiers half ardent to keep animals? (8)
10 Dined at a hotel as is natural (6)
12 A clown turns shy (5)
13 Wight? (4,2,3)
14 Garlic phobia may be related to life (12)
18 Scores make a crew for shooting (12)
21 Wealthy male entertains oriental in government building (9)
23 Boy — one taken in by a bird (5)
24 Good ship in the mud (6)
25 A terrible thing, bad art round the town (8)
26 It anaesthetises the figure (6)
27 A lady without a place to sleep in a novel (4,4)

Down

1 Pay the artillery; don't yield outside (6)
2 Part of a service prior to Monday? (6)
3 ... and grunt of hounds? (3,2,4)
4 Labour? It has a mandate for a job (7,5)
6 It takes two to make the sun's effects disappear (5)
7 Seeing a wrong sum in a short distance (8)
8 Where to putt with cleverness? It's a pest (8)
11 Cheated girls of good looks? (5-7)
15 Toils awkwardly amid damage from hard fall (9)
16 A man without a name across the ocean (8)
17 Linked at the elbows (3,2,3)
19 In spite of the degree, vermin! (6)
20 In a frenzy men find a catalyst (6)
22 In which to eat the passover (5)

38

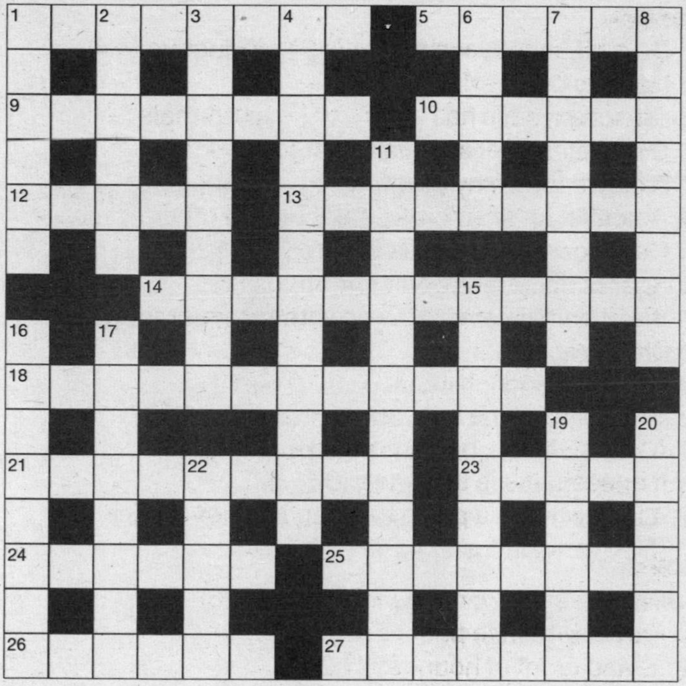

Across

1 He's 16 to begin with, among the most holy — an awfully pi RC (8,6)

8 She's a vermin (5)

9 He's alternatively an outsider to a Scot (8)

11 Old weapon for a student — be difficult about it (7)

12 Ascetic, an aristocratic saint before (7)

13 She goes onwards, as it were (5)

15 Uncordial sort of pourer (4,5)

17 Died horribly after a game with the Pentagon? (4-5)

20 26's teacher (5)

21 "Hooray and ____ she ______" (7)

23 Predatory person reverses dramatic role (7)

25 Evidences of guilt are in the bond (8)

26 Start tickling to defeat the fish (5)

27 Call for applause for song made to re-echo by German admiral (5,4,5)

Down

1 20 plus 4? (5,3,4)

2 See 6

3 Sees bones? Not in this condition! (9)

4 Arranged on purpose? (2,5)

5 Possible beginning of vice-captain's confession (7)

6,2 A revolution on the River Test (10)

7 Carnivore swallows broken beak at its mooring? (5,4)

10 Journalist who sounds like Heine? (6,6)

14 Give another coat to the Venerable Harris? (9)

16 Two creatures in charge of purifying (9)

18 Ruffle most of Diana's headdress (7)

19 Vacillating, I keep the inside free of water (7)

22,24 Rocket with a copper base? (5,5)

39

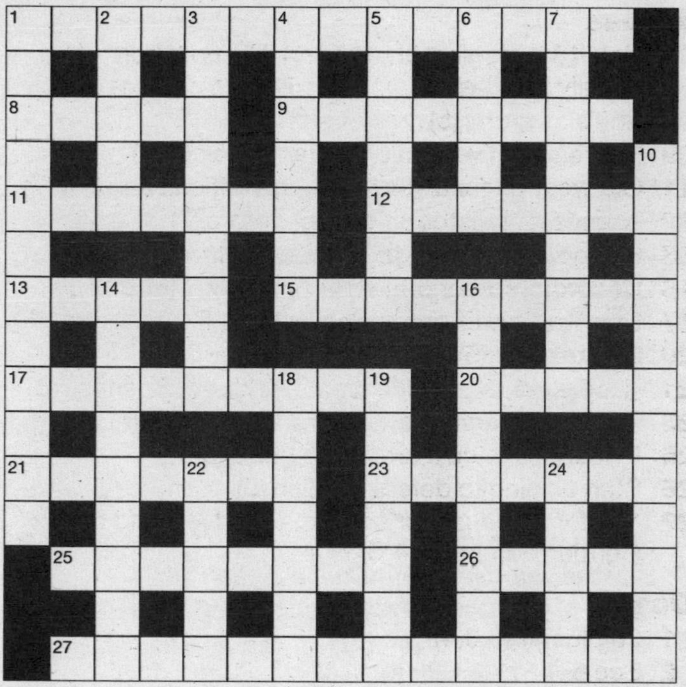

Across

1 Hamlet's barbarian ancestry (4,11)
8 Old car took part of Oxford college to Baltic port (8)
9 Mere key to cockney light? (6)
10 Cold region in which to dice with life? (3,5)
11 Pole short of money is engaged? (6)
13 Haricot? (6,4)
16 Withdrawal may cause endless contrariety (10)
19 Out to know the Scots when alarmed? (6)
20 Tyrannical place, first in the month (8)
21 Not extramural? (6)
22 A Commie's inclined to partial unconsciousness (8)
23 Pre-war encounter of two of a kind (I don't quote) (5,5,5)

Down

1 Wanted: something for the 15 is inverted (8,7)
2 Prize turns up in chest (6)
3 Ban the world in little faith (6)
4 Order of infrequent occurrence about a sort of glue (10)
5 Time to reveal with gilt (8)
6 Cool down? Risk it! (8)
7 Civilisation was introduced by Chris, wandering round a river with a bird (3,7,5)
12 Confused by the wrong coin, he accepts payment (10)
14 Come down on both sides when led astray by a fiddle (8)
15 Medical records of holder and reserve? (8)
17 Leap year's 19-ing (6)
18 Soothe with a blow (6)

40

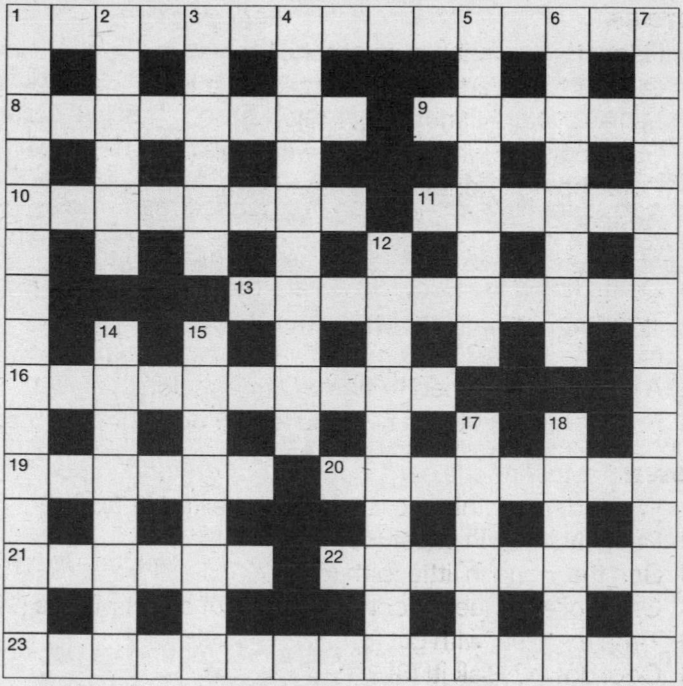

Solve the clues and fit them in where they will go.

A weaves a web when a man of renown gets inside a musician (7)
B is a plate for controlling the flow, or perhaps a magician (7)
C is a process in kitchen: in study a month has just started (7)
D had just started to phone, but when everyone entered departed (7)
E is a strait for New Yorkers, an egghead: a man who's contending (4,5)
F, which may lead to explosions, with little French customs is blending (5)
G is a speech of farewell, which reveals how to guide by misguiding (3,2,4,3)
H is a town that plays football; you'll find it in Yorkshire's West Riding (12,7)
I must be steep for one mile and a river comes endlessly after (7)
J, what the fool on the card does, is not unconnected with laughter (5,7)
K for the pieces with handles, or dark times for anyone listening (7)
L seems a wish for a first class return to find bliss at a christening (7)
M, a Wagnerian voice, sends Artillery's regiments packing (12)
N's later Tertiary period: in Peterborough's stream I am backing (7)
O's a French city that's not on the level with gold to begin it (7)
P's on the level, French city — the recently dead are within it (7)
Q's for a change been as inquests on creatures of sculpture majestic (6,6)
R's going headlong in Scotland: male creatures, one Scots and domestic (7)
S, the farceur on the street, is a genus that ululates nightly (5)
T, after dining, leave café in haste to play cricket more brightly? (3,3,3)
U for increased unemployment to characterise otiosity (7)
V is a job for the Sultan — to wit, that is, cost or velocity (9)
W. West was cut down and grew bigger, like certain moustaches (5)
X is descried back in Dorset or Exmoor: the body it parches (7)
Y will emerge from the fray and the foe for sabbatical session (4,3)
Z the philosopher's case upon Tamburlaine made an impression (9)

41

Across

7 Quick! It's the mushroom man! (7)
8 Sack after a lot of talk? (3,4)
10 Cause of Dutch courage? (6)
11 Economise on the Sappers' dugout (8)
12,22 You don't often meet Heyerdahl's flying boats? (4,4)
13 Eccentric missile in a 23 (10)
14 Uncontrolled fight — it's a plant (11)
19 Uncontrolled fight — no one charged (4,3,3)
22 See 12
23 Doctor takes grated carrot for a pollutant (5,3)
24 Chap who stops the train? (6)
25 Bird on the point of invading Britain (7)
26 Not quite complete and not all flattering (7)

Down

1 Junction for uncritical theatregoers? (7)
2 A rye blended with milk pudding once upon a time (5,3)
3 Cupid's turning to rice (6)
4 Standard bearer? (8)
5 A short fare in the tree again (6)
6 Torture, in fury, 201 (7)
9 The way down to destruction in Kent? (11)
15 Prove there's something to answer? (8)
16 Might be fit in no time at all — by lying on one side? (8)
17 He swears the news is about nothing and the wrong way round (7)
18 Cover up a girl with horns (7)
20 Stop! That's one up to "Disgusted" (6)
21 Antenatal party (6)

42

Across

1 Melancholy can pull us on ahead without aristocratic verve (14)
9 Unknown, possibly, the only hope for such as 27? (9)
10 The central light (5)
11 Plants are about to do one (5)
12 But what price America without me in it? (5,4)
13 Allow meat in Lincolnshire (8)
14 Possibly is left to this (6)
17 Incessantly leading to Rome? (6)
19 The last home may get them (with luck) (3,5)
22 Wrinkles on the brow of a journalist? (9)
24 Times for such as 27 (5)
25 Desert, the journalist thought (5)
26 For writing a brief line on a delivery note? (6,3)
27 Scotsman, retired man, nomadic Arabs and Irish musicians (10,4)

Down

1 People who are wordy and awfully prolix cheer gas! (14)
2 Girl on her head in Poland (7)
3 Scots roll — it's a test for a christening (9)
4 Well protected from cold and rain? (8)
5 Hard on the royal pillow? (6)
6 New York like a lake (5)
7 It's heavenly under a tree (7)
8 Rabbit fed snake — so it didn't have to get up! (9,2,3)
15 Siren takes me from 24 to Hair (9)
16 Our Lancashire edition is diplomatic (8)
18 More leaves much to be desired here? (4,3)
20 On Monday morning one first wants the strong stuff (7)
21 An orderly county (6)
23 Burdened student with a study (5)

43

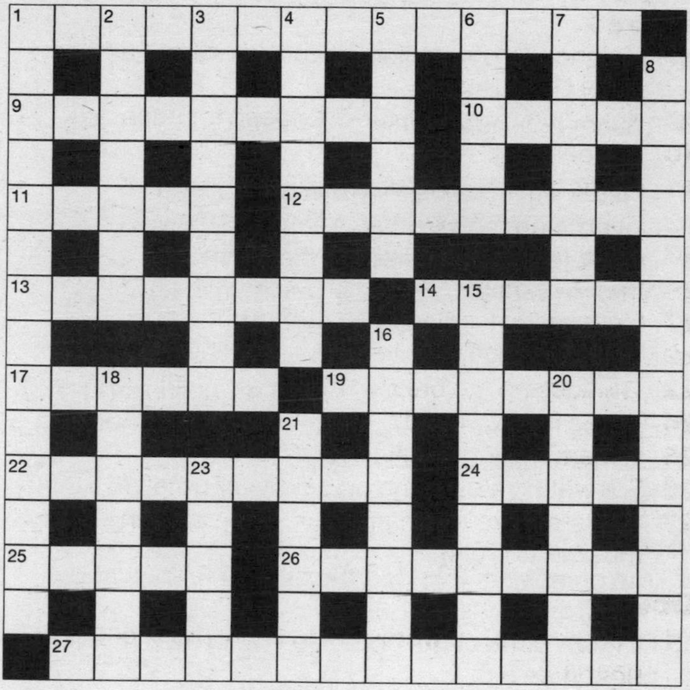

Across

8 Maltreatment by some bacillus before time (3-5)
9 Rating for ability? (6)
10 It takes coal as a matter of course (6)
11 Herb's girls (8)
12 Ecclesiastical name for Rusk or Acheson (4)
13 Not enough food to give crumbs? (10)
15 One object in a hundred on the palm? (7)
16 A month without church, a year on fish (7)
18 In "A Maria" the A is for Joseph (10)
19 Nobody sounds religious (4)
20 Male witch found during a short day in Holland (3,5)
22 Biblical measures: hogshead in reversed shape (6)
23 Uninteresting nonsense? (3,3)
24 No is on it (8)

Down

1 The curses confounded the glory of France about here (15)
2 German book about champion radio men has one about here (15)
3 Like the Holy of Holies (10)
4 Scene of farce and boredom? (7)
5 The river god seems to have two lives (4)
6 Do they sell cars and have birds to let here? (15)
7 Veronica ran hers about here (15)
14 A bank-note's used for perfuming snuff (5,5)
17 Musical confusion of CE and EC (7)
21 Walk (we hear) through it (4)

44

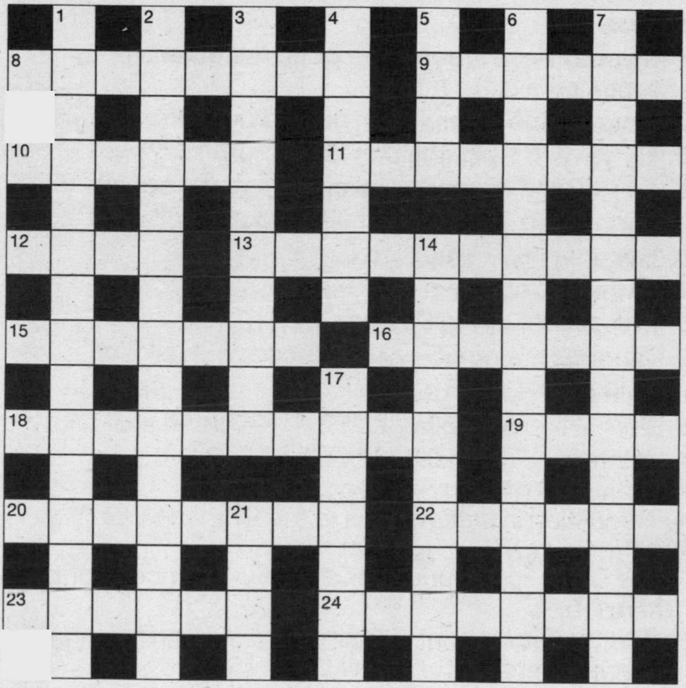

Across

1 Mystic trance around one pole: the other's toothsome (14)
9 Increase the potential of the middle of the channels (7)
10 He painted a pig: the painting's horrific! (7)
11 Worthy and deserving folk return to the subject (5)
12 Funny man, Lucius, not suited to the Halls? (9)
13 Record spot – a real find (9)
14 Father X's church plate (5)
15 Famous refusal to Edward (5)
17 Composer's wine — or composer with a lot of spiders (9)
20 Breakfast food to ruin a sick Frenchman (9)
22 Marx is not 12 — the weapon's not on (5)
23 Indian princess in American state gets it on the brain (7)
24 Reduction in Indian dress in the Crimean War (7)
25 Modesty, so to speak (14)

Down

1 The Marines return — many do — to the Indian Civil Service, famous for its laws (14)
2 Bill can't stand a faithful friend (7)
3 One's cool when one's blood runs cold? (9)
4 Carry out capital punishment (7)
5 Back in 24 hours from Africa (7)
6 Drink for African emperor (5)
7 Fruit and cereal, endlessly, in a vessel (7)
8 He's kind enough to give the pith, short and plain (14)
14 Have a game of bingo and where? (9)
16 Queen in transport in the country (7)
17 Second birds go to the dogs (7)
18 It's in London, otherwise in tea (7)
19 Headless post in gilt (7)
21 Stay an attempt to point (5)

45

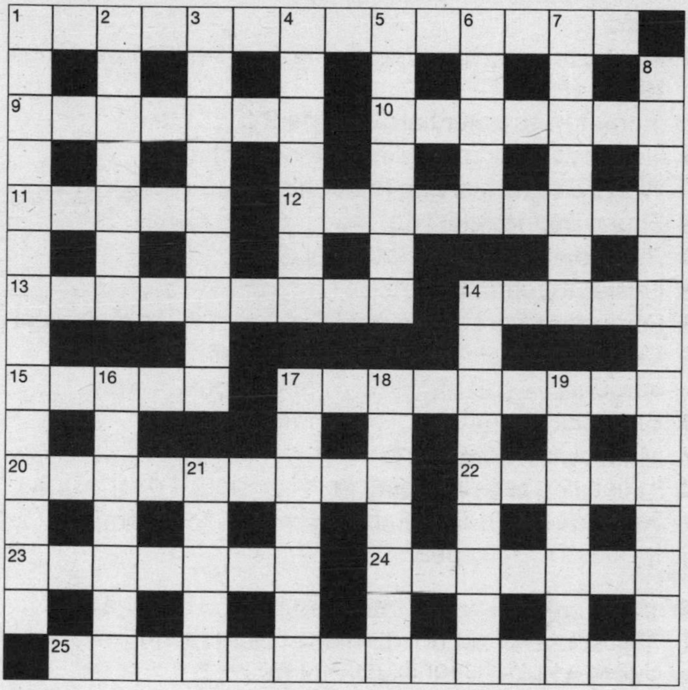

Across

1 Rubber mat with pile, keeping cool even when things are ... (13)
10 ... on top of one by arrangement (9)
11 Literary 24 takes ship in gratitude (5)
12 Italy's capital in the revolution? (5)
13 Prizewinning goat? (9)
14 The quiet sound of a lot of talk (7)
16 Lost and found in London (7)
18 A result of the sun: no mistake about it, it's diabolical (7)
20 Grain, a measure for the university (7)
21 Aggressive sort of culture, not without love (9)
23 Not for long (5)
24 Beast with more 'eat (5)
25 Use oil rig in a strict way (9)
26 "The Importance of Being Earnest", for example? (4,4,5)

Down

2 Is the creditor within intended to be a criminal? (9)
3 The sound of school dinners should be (5)
4 Let him bleed a bit — without this? (7)
5 Restored to the grid? (7)
6 Dealest? (3,6)
7 Where to put on a 26? (5)
8 Neighbourly settlement to join up with taxis? (13)
9 River god with round table — go back in for a ringer (13)
15 Dramatic character with two wives (9)
17 Old city's business — nothing in fashion (9)
19 Old city turns into birdsong — don't despair! (5,2)
20 Spanish boy following a pet (7)
22 Bird leaves jauntily (5)
23 Animal to leave concealed, as they say (5)

46

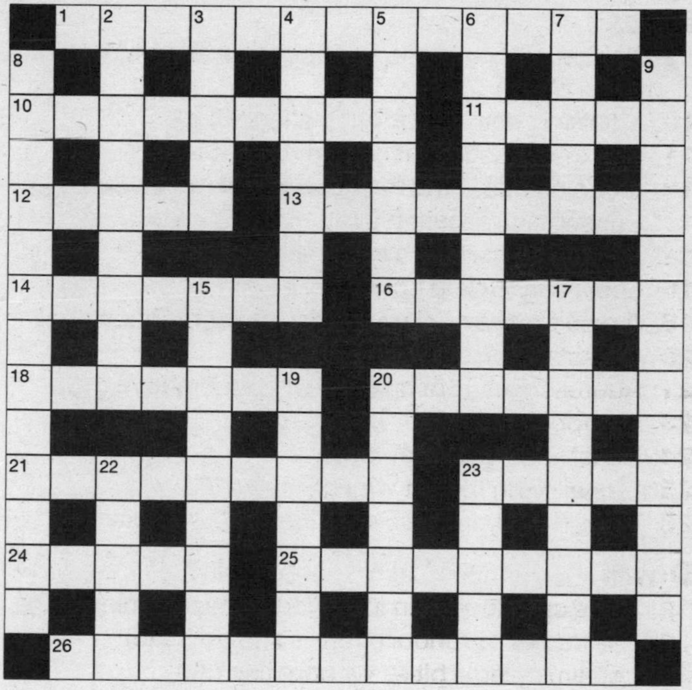

Across

1,5,10 Nut, some of it in dry dock, for a climbing mouse (7,7,4)
11 Something new at the local: cheers! (10)
12 In the local I could get cotton (6)
13 Soft going underfoot: worried about the favourite (8)
14 Counsel is given when 9 (9)
16 Prophetess is upset by student (5)
17 Permission to go (5)
19 Standard article, without help, on segregation (9)
23 Worcester's principal fruit (8)
24 Starve – get something to eat about morning (6)
26 The mood all over the world (10)
27 Sequel to 8? Yes and no (4)
28,29 Our TV on the way to France? (7,7)

Down

2 With such unpunctuality I keep in 14 (7)
3 Indian knife, turned to annoy Britain, sounds just the thing for the kitchen! (5)
4 Maybe very expensive for us in our turn (7)
6 Clothing of the boys, lily-white for example (6)
7 Among friends X is playful (9)
8 Colony rhyming with 3? (7)
9 Dance cum piano? On the contrary! (13)
15 Vital spot for something connected with football … (9)
18 … where it's always going to the North (7)
20 Judge about to demand silence will brighten up (7)
21 Son and heir turning away from the sea (7)
22 University of Cambridge leaders get fed up (6)
25 Indian people get on (5)

47

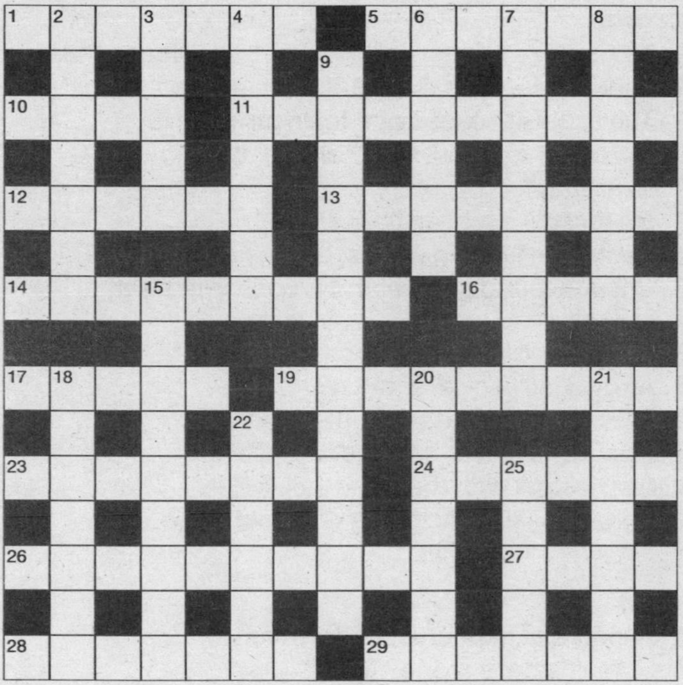

Across

1 Workaday sayings, but they have an edge to them (8)
5 A theologian was the guide — that's bad! (6)
9 The acquisitiveness of a town on strike (8)
10 Girl about to throw softly all over the world (6)
11 Host with tenant (8)
12 Bill for little cash, as they say (6)
14 Reduction in plain words, or he will accuse (10)
18 Change round and Ireland is concerned with animals (10)
22 Some people are now near to fame (6)
23 Arrowsmith, the dramatist? (8)
24 The rest of the letter's in the pink (6)
25 The old have it at heart to be upset (8)
26 Also jesting with the prince (6)
27 Prince shaking the sides of his cot in the neighbourhood (8)

Down

1 Announcer kept artist in detention (6)
2 Horse dealer's stone? (6)
3 The French get upset at a left-wing emblem (6)
4 How to perform a christening at the seaside? (10)
6 Tact for a gourmet? (8)
7 The words of the title, brother? (8)
8 A cover-up for right-wing dallying (8)
13 Old Moore, perhaps, about to go up after an endless walk (10)
15 There's no 21 in some cricket nobody won (8)
16 St Patrick's around and won't make concessions (5,3)
17 Northern 4 inverted in the island (8)
19 Still discharging? (6)
20 The win might be purifying (6)
21 Believe a journalist in a review (6)

48

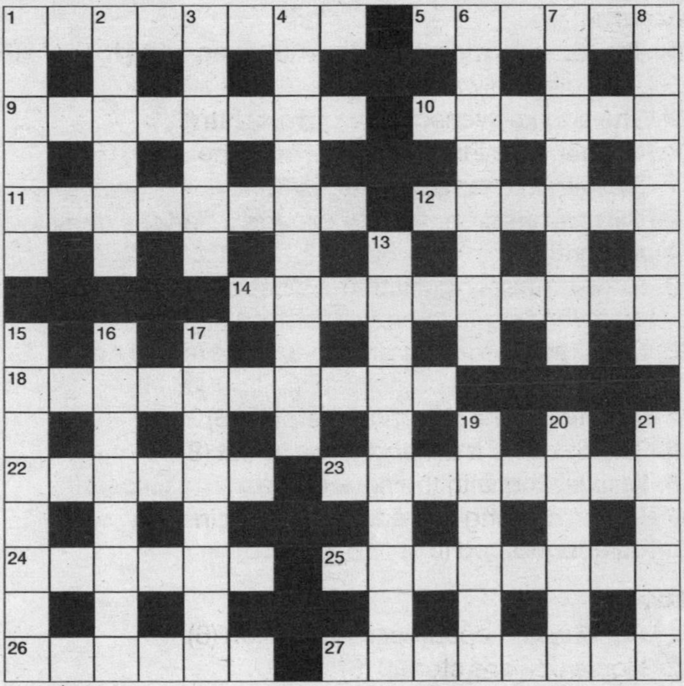

Across

1 Ghostly form of Samantha about page 50 (10)
6 Like an MA? (6)
9 Where to keep crockery for the table (8)
10 Prosper — like dusty white stuff? (8)
11 Orb with key indicates Venus (6)
12 Remove head from straw hat and insert the detested object (8)
14 Some money to go with the Water Music? (8)
16 It doesn't hurt to overtake without crossing the line (8)
19 It's upset me to have died in two ways and not be a ghost (8)
21 Stick to the demon drink! (6)
22 Green appearance of bare bone (8)
23 It's likely that a plebeian is entertaining Gilbert (8)
24 Beginning with failure at cricket and tennis? (6)
25 Franciscans of the old school (10)

Down

1 Where one can hear fish? (6)
2 Supremely waggish (4)
3 Reducing the circle after the end of the race (8)
4 It's bootless to be in them (10,4)
5 A burglar about to steal a tumbler (7)
7 Decision of a class (6)
8 Ruin of beauty — ban sin to repair it (9,5)
13 Take unfair advantage by rail (5)
15 Animals surround church doctor in winter (8)
17 Does he want to get married?
18 First and second from Germany — ergo, a change (6)
20 Thus the caterpillar's back in Spain (6)
22 Five-year-old rising star (4)

49

Across

1 22 bluntly so-called (6)
5 22 shillings and pence — not a girl returning to her best friend (8)
9 Not 1, 5 across, 10, or 21 — or hindquarters? (2,6)
10 22 man with a certain degree (6)
11 Where to go for an ornament for a 54 mess shirt? (12)
13 10 should be, and that's a fact (4)
14 Instrument for turning a French corpse to a bit of a skeleton (8)
17 Loud noise won't change scene of prosperity (4,4)
18 Low farewell (4)
20 Neither church nor cinema get together on paper (7,5)
23 Nettled — sounds like a riding cap (6)
24 Mixed our mixture to begin with (8)
25 China — she will be provoking at first (8)
26 Present what happened at high table? (6)

Down

2 Land scheme (4)
3 River water boiled by local representatives (5,4)
4 The likeness is going back a long way (6)
5 Easy for Virgil, harrowing for Christian theology? (7,4,4)
6 Sticking a bill, he's got one on (8)
7 Beast all right with a relation (5)
8 Wife's relation giving a telling off (5,5)
12 Ignore cost in treating wood (10)
15 Like a cow with no tail and a wild dog to the north of Hertfordshire (9)
16 Post Office girder destroyed at breakfast time (8)
19 A lodge of consequence historically (3-3)
21 22 can be joined (5)
22 Fit to wear (4)

50

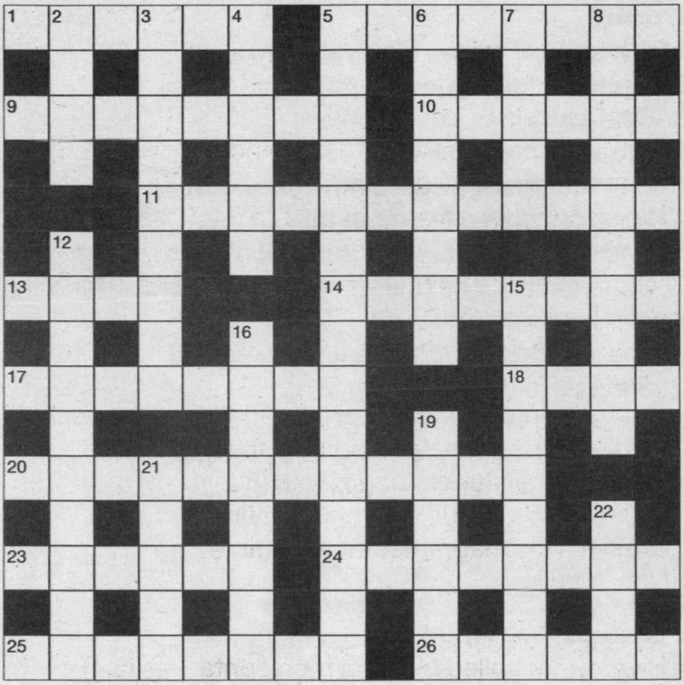

Across

1 4 for a 10 across — equivalent to 2000? (8,5)
9 Goddess follows in a state (7)
10 One going in to join up? (7)
11 Agree on the score (5)
12 Be in charge of a successful show? Bull's eye! (6,3)
13 Requirements often must (5)
15 Bad men have the edge in a Lincolnshire upheaval (9)
17 Statement that seems extreme to an establishment (9)
18 Black island's return (5)
19 The life and soul'd make a real fire! (5,4)
22 Surrey's fringe is winning (2,3)
23 Make use of a feat (7)
24 The beast sounds learned and precious (3,4)
25 4 for a 10 across — winner at first light? (8,5)

Down

2 Allowing scope to dig tunnel (9)
3 Source of inclination to type (5)
4 Present conflict in the present age (5)
5 Pickers are wrong-headed, heartless ecclesiastics (9)
6 An infinite darkness is not far off (5)
7,10,22 4 for 10 across — made out a plan for worship? (13,7,5)
8 It's a hanging matter in wild brier: its 22 down's a 4 (7,6)
10 See 7
14 Walk confidently — drink when about to get a lift (6,3)
15 Guide, if 7, leads to a 4 (7)
16 Woman judge at the bar turning one hair (9)
20 Singular speaker, relation to a painter (5)
21 Grub of particular value (5)
22 See 7

51

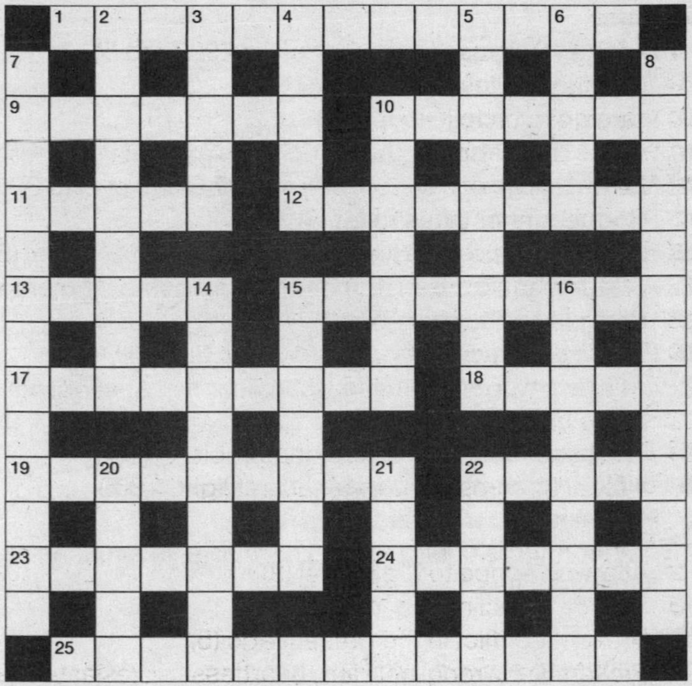

Across

1 Monk(ey) (8)
5 Sporting contest at the Oval? (3-3)
9 Manage to hide in covert (8)
10 From “The Return of the Cenci”, a classical verse form (6)
11 Not as follows? (14)
14 Pair the runner takes to (5)
15 It’s never possible to have audacity (5)
16 A chap who acts for another chap (5)
17 Word play about transport (5)
20 Return of heavenly food in Vietnam (5)
22 Let’s ’ave reforms in penal establishments — individual tuition (7,7)
24 The gunners are home and dry (6)
25 Wicked amount of Russian paper indeed (8)
26 Preliminary to a bottle of rum (2-2-2)
27 Father returns during mother’s trouble, in a manner of speaking (8)

Down

1 Prepare to shoot a bird (4)
2 How to make up for extreme loss from Cornish town (7)
3 Motorworks? (7)
4 Besiege one entrance and ask questions (11)
6 See 19
7 See 18
8 Awkward, shy, cramped, insensitive brutes (10)
12 Rum queen, Queen Elizabeth I, maybe from 21 in 3 (11)
13 Liberal in insurance? (5,5)
18,7 Right — it’s hot and cold in a braggart, the dirty one in 3 (7,7)
19,6 Is he on about bitterness after a stretch, the stately one in 3? (7,7)
20 Fool turning up vague in the land of … (7)
21 … 9 5: is that right? (7)
23 River, or poem on one (4)

52

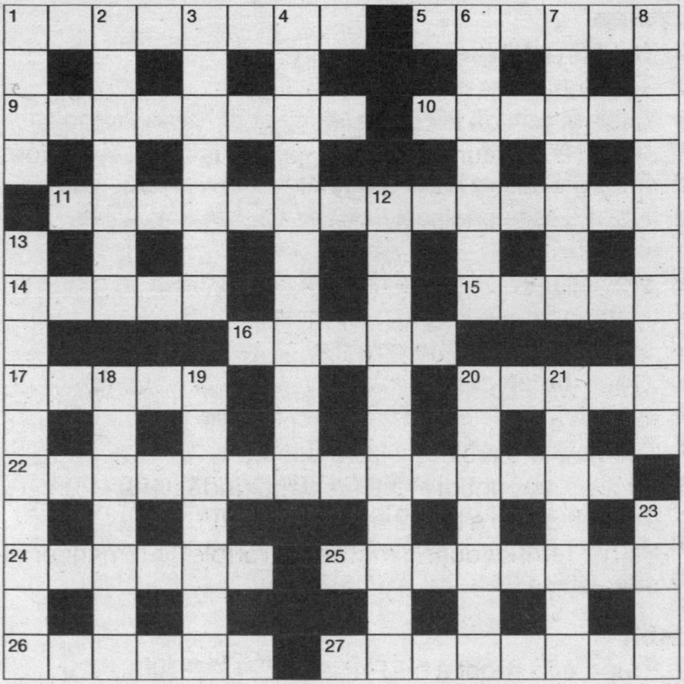

Across

1 No. 3 in a tangle with a maid (6)
4 The sign of an actress (6)
9 Luckily, put 24, it's unusual for chef having to do with beggary (2,3,5,2,3)
10 Political philosopher's books kept by weeders (6)
11 No. 4 kisses endlessly, wildly, for fun out of the cold (5-3)
12 No. 9's new valet has large stake in old card game (8)
14 Fishing for alcohol ban by airline? (3-3)
15 Prince in Old Contemptibles' part (6)
18 No. 7, otherwise 9, with the last of the soup (8)
21 Hairstyle for the élite with lots of calories (5,3)
22 No. 10's greeting for C to C, say (6)
24 Pi style Shakespearean opening can change one character (Bill) to another (Christopher) (15)
25 Almost Nelson's last words to time and fate (6)
26 No. 12 set deer back on edge (6)

Down

1 No. 5 with more than 16 feet amid the dancers (7)
2 King and captain with Biblical harlot (5)
3 No. 8 has suet cooked by Frenchman (7)
5 Moved on when acquitted (7)
6 Behaviour causing long sentence at women's prison, say (4,5)
7 Not started work in raised glass tube (7)
8 No. 1 at a party in India (6)
13 Social events in homestead, ancestral hall, or whatever (3,6)
16 Single out a listener to the gospel (7)
17 No. 2 to cause annoyance of high degree (7)
18 No. 6, 1, or less (6)
19 Like a sign of an 11th century pope (7)
20 No. 11 — she's French — in short stories (7)
23 Elephant's chest? (5)

53

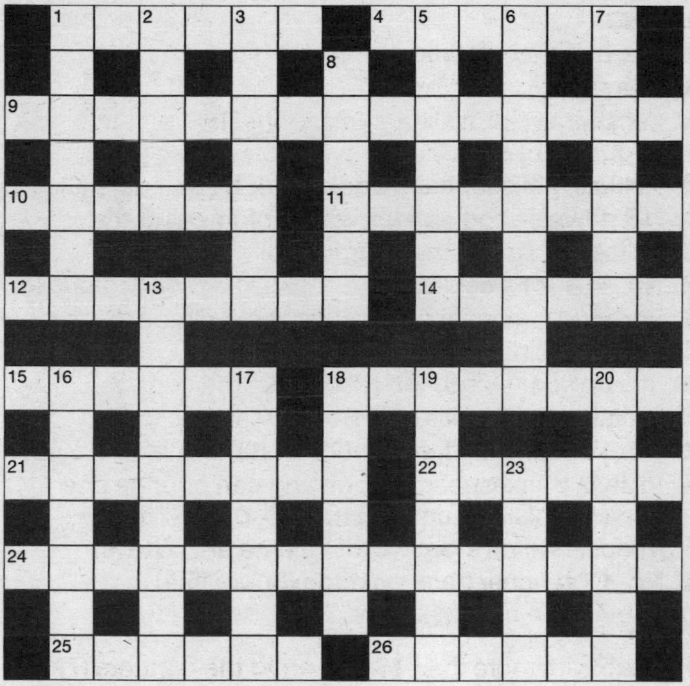

Across

1 Partial cure: JP died as a result (10)
8 See 11
10 Neither aye or no (10)
11,8 Scene of mutiny and revolution whose point is critical (2,6)
13 13 down's short holiday opens old wound (7)
15 Subject of a test that's drawn (6)
16 Washer for a cable (6)
17 Seconds, more or less, round the cosmos call for aid (5,5,5)
18 It's down wrong in the record (6)
20 An idée not fixe for a poem (6)
21 Neptune's attendants sound commonplace creatures (7)
22 See 26
25 Go sightseeing somewhere in S-Switzerland in a maul (6-4)
26,22 God houses a famous advocate (8,4)
27 Going to a ball? Take her pen and sign (10)

Down

2,3 Study simply to adapt (8)
4 Some children change when they get wet (6)
5 River in China submerged lines in television (7-3,5)
6 Camptown chorus returning had nothing to do at first (6)
7 Undifferentiated? (10)
9 The posh aristocrat was a waiter incognito (10)
12 Almost isolated (10)
13 L and three successive letters form a depression (7)
14 Draws a cracksman (7)
15 Engagement with church music? (6,4)
19 Dissatisfied bird (6)
20 A spanner for lawlessness (6)
23,24 Gives birth to a family on Guard? (8)

54

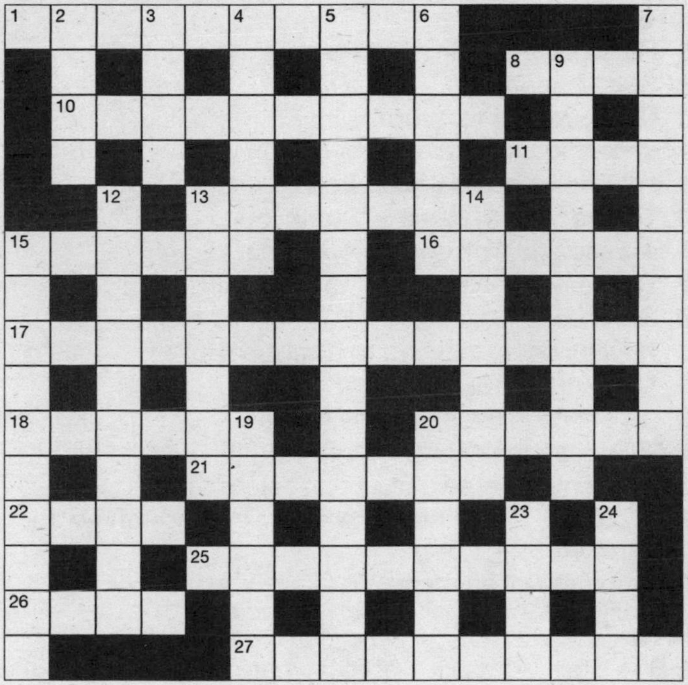

Across

1 His work is deriving from one Tolstoy gem (11)
8 See 11 and 24
10 I was anxious to return, with Etna erupting, to do some digging (10)
11,8 23 work seems the obvious one to me (8)
14 To lose head in panic is wrong (5)
15 Agreement in an endeavour to eat (6)
17 Redeemer generally has to appear (6)
19 Silver age? (6-4,5)
20 Revolutionary in 5 has to disappear (6)
22 Magical bird (6)
23 It's put on in the next race (5)
24,8 Rescue the enemy? (4,4)
27 Some moment to bring in an establishment (10)
28,11,25,26 Apple pudding again, produce of the tree to reform (4,4,1,3,4)
29 Empress not suspect? (7,4)

Down

2,3 8's fellow has 24's object where the water was (8)
4 Menial want to upset you (6)
5 Sweeping things again into lesser shape (15)
6 Swift work at the day of wrath? (6)
7 Listen to the provocative way Milton described Mirth (5-6)
9 B. Levin upset about a song that doesn't change (10)
12 Say when people call (5,6)
13 Emphatically not HP (5-5)
16 He gives us the bird (5)
18 A month to live, perhaps (5)
21 Her intention was upset — by Puck? (6)
22 A thing to be of 27 (6)
25,26 See 28

55

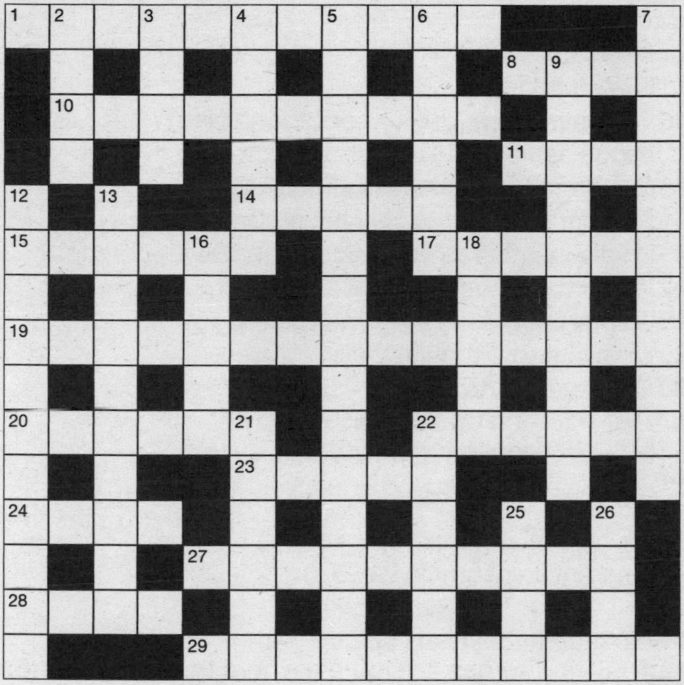

Across

9 Minor OT patient? (6,3)
10 Fast nothing! It's slow! (5)
11 First, it isn't the girl; it's somebody else (7)
12 Loose as absolute certs often come (7)
13 Goodbye to the model batman? (5)
14 Popular hit out of focus with cues (6,3)
16 Ersatz weathercock's nest is withdrawn, perhaps (6,2,3,4)
19 It's for the rest of 2 (6,3)
21 Godmother to the king and queen? (5)
22 US claim to a show (7)
23 Prophet entertaining sailors in East Yorks (7)
24 Birds (of the 1) come 23 down to (5)
25 Monument to the doctor's manner (9)

Down

1 It's rash to show lead's livid (3-7)
2 Itinerant saint on the wave (8)
3 Out of date, like Panama? (3,3)
4 A container that isn't sealed (4)
5 When the lights went out (died, fused), the cat got in (10)
6 Telescope lens? (5,3)
7 English disease upset swallow (6)
8 See 23
14 A catchword in more senses than one (10)
15 "22 down 8 for the ______, 11 9 for the 25 21 across" (old music-hall song) (10)
17 Striking beasts? (8)
18 Likes not change in Derbyshire (8)
20 Result of a lob? (6)
21 Gold in a lump of bog (6)
22 Oliver's Utopian request (4)
23,8 Domestic service? (8)

56

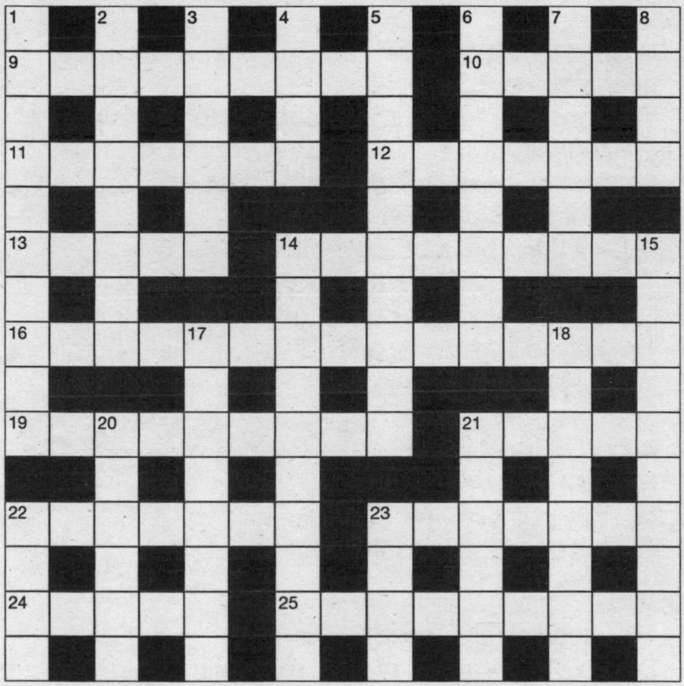

Across

9 Wishful thinking: there'll be little change from a hearin' aid (4,2,3)

10 "Tomorrow to fresh _____, and pastures new" (Milton) (5)

11 An American test unfinished in Europe (7)

12 Moor of battle adds weight of war (7)

13,22 Anything but a quick profit (4,4)

14 To my epoch I appear to be making legends (10)

16 Historian of voyages on the Tay with a hulk? (7)

17 Be likely to take one's post (5,2)

19 Will that's passed (10)

22 See 13

24 A third of a detective? (7)

25 He doth know, presumably (7)

26,23 Tory point of view? (5,5)

27 Girl in 10 turning a poultice (9)

Down

1 Tautological reasons (3,3,9)

2 Dance's change of direction results in a lot of shocks (8)

3 Use saltpetre when there's a louse about (5)

4 Chemical reaction of an animal on a table, say (8)

5 Kai Lung's creator gives Dracula's satisfaction (6)

6 Southern puns on fencing (9)

7,8 Wrongly state second shot's third: complete details (3,3,2,3,5,3,2)

15 Bound to get awfully busy about the elevation (9)

17 Keep cannabis in the kitchen (8)

18 Tubman eats and upsets himself inside (8)

20 Cake of soap? (6)

21 Kind of sequel to the steam engine? (6)

23 See 26

57

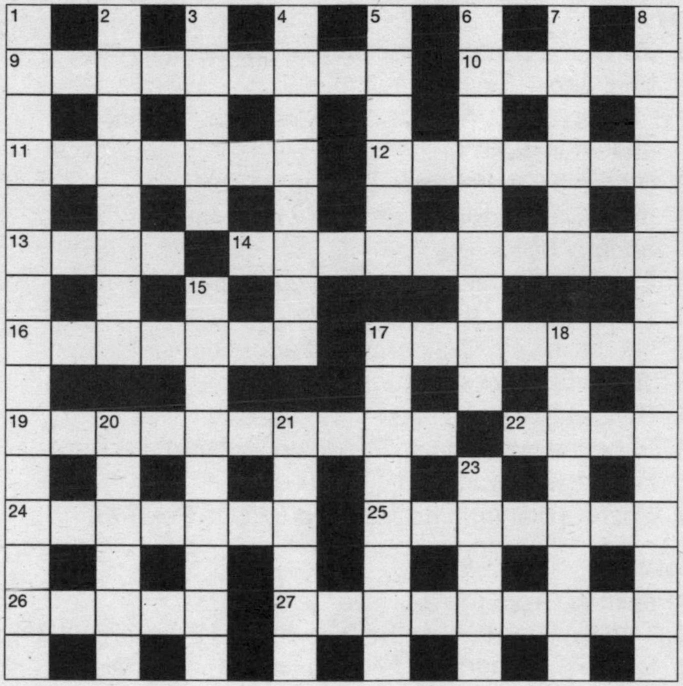

Across

1 Kurdistan certainly has a lot of space (8)
5 That goose look? (6)
9,10 One certainly is a bit lacking in the fashion for adventure (8,6)
12 Died in prison — try to get money (5)
13 Vessel in reactor to come down in Mausoleum country (9)
14 Old soldier's taken prisoner, back part in front (12)
18 Picture of one left by purge (12)
21 Vendee's satisfied comment about hunt (9)
23 Tree insect's companion (5)
24 Sense utter fool's inside (6)
25 Is there a faint possibility gown is on crooked? (8)
26 Decide to colonise (6)
27 Political diarist to go from Douglas to Peel? (8)

Down

1 Remove from the aide-de-camp (6)
2,3 Walking out since the lady is: hold it there! (6,2,3,4)
4 Single pet at old city is in a fix over the top drawer (12)
6 Latin skill applied to crime (5)
7 Harangue to help rising clan (8)
8 Blushing, as opposed to pale-skinned in North America (3-5)
11 Incendiary device — put a lot of jewels right into river (5-7)
15 Agitated for lower and upper garments to be shortened (9)
16 What God does comes to an end without concessions being raised (8)
17 Pipe through which blood goes round inside (8)
19 Edward I's hesitating, having no interest (6)
20 Japanese ruler has weapon with bone sawn off (6)
22 Keen on the Spanish pub (5)

58

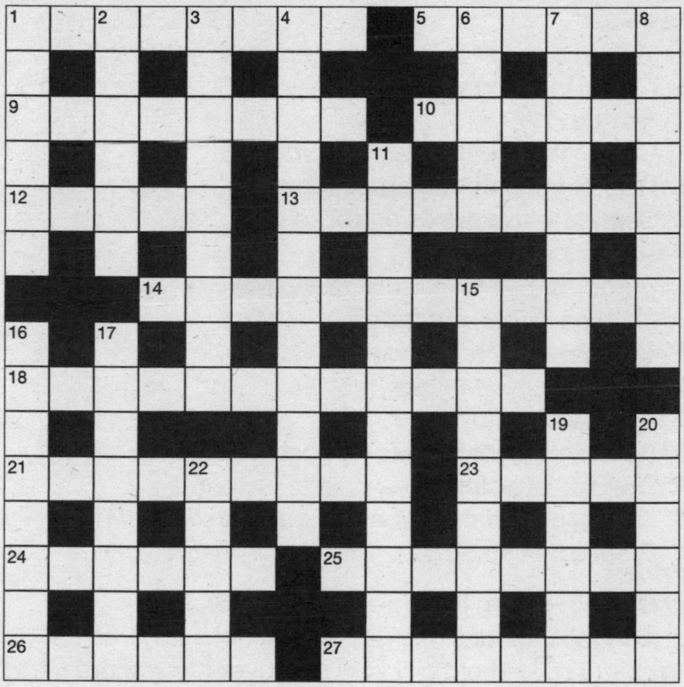

Across

1 1lb hot rum left, maybe, but no room left (4,2,3,4)
8 United Nations vehicle for Peter's old pence on bare boards (10)
9 Consequently, the giant returns (4)
11 Rout formed about girl who tumbled a dictator (8)
12 Destination of ashes on the last day? (6)
14 A wire for foxes (5)
15 South Africa's over there: keep talking! (3,2)
16 Love partly for students (5)
17 Submarine or subterranean dog (5)
20 Runs elusively on high? (5)
22 Source of 18 (6)
23 Bachelor doctor I meet through a musician (8)
25 Dead? I pray for him — a little water (4)
26 She tells of a deception without unveiling at once (10)
27 Pathetic sailor obtains things hard to hit (6,7)

Down

1 It weighs a stone (8-7)
2 Lake in France with somewhat queer surface ... (7)
3 ... won't get like a lake in the North of England? (7)
4 6, 16, 14, 10, 20 down, 12, 22, 21 and 17 (3,7)
5 River garden (4)
6 Liquid copper, happy about it! (7)
7 Feign sorrows' end (anag) — but they return the morning after (5,4,6)
10 God at arms? (4)
13 Indirect form of junction (10)
18 Source of power gives posh princess hesitation (7)
19 It's our responsibility (4)
20 Ruler of heaven, de jure, without hell (7)
21 His is sea air after the writer returns (7)
24 Profit without a trap (4)

59

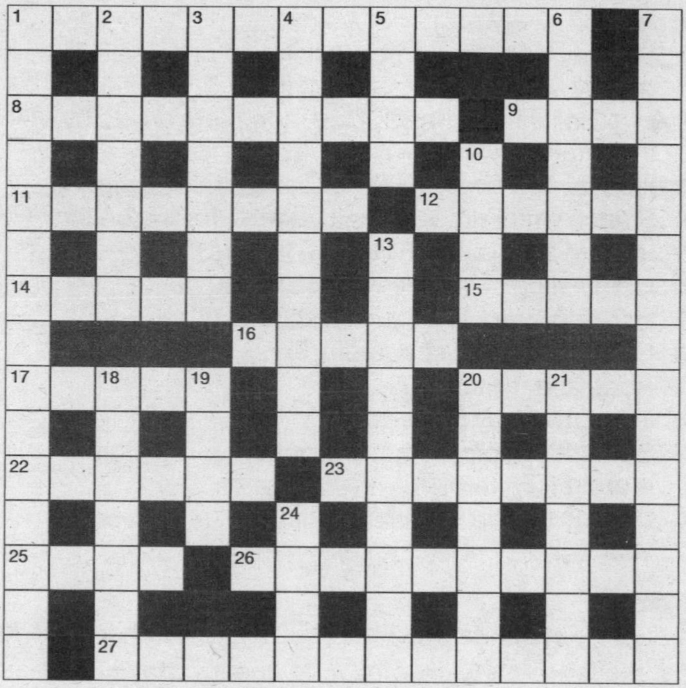

Across

1,27 Tory left a messy confusion and one where wise men get the country to work by ... (5,2,7,3,11)

8,9 ... ear without, thank God, complete article by incomplete poet (5,5,3)

11 Honest as a goalpost (7)

12 French writer dressed as a nude — for the beach? (7)

13 Pattern for a poem in Roman figures (5)

15 Cardinal point in a wealthy place (9)

17 Borough associated with Oxbrick? (9)

20 Observation of a spectacle (5)

21 Rude and military? (7)

23 Deceptive way of feeding (7)

25 Something spicy to read about the pub before morning (8)

26 Decline to return poor old coin (5)

27 See 1

Down

1 Scene of murders in 1 across 27 — a deathly place for the herb (3,3,6)

2 The king's upset the beer (5)

3 He can't keep up with Lloyd George's garret (9)

4 More colourless way to use butter (7)

5 Non-white bag of coal, sky showing (4,3)

6 Wood sticking out from No. 10 (5)

7 Making a fresh start with a professional engine (9)

10 I end up in trouble after a month with 8 9's detective (7,5)

14 Something taken by a detective (9)

16 Die a saint in Clive's company (4,5)

18 Puzzle how to cover up a book (7)

19 FND? (7)

22 Painter's place incorporated in 6 (5)

24 I cry up a Biblical character (5)

60

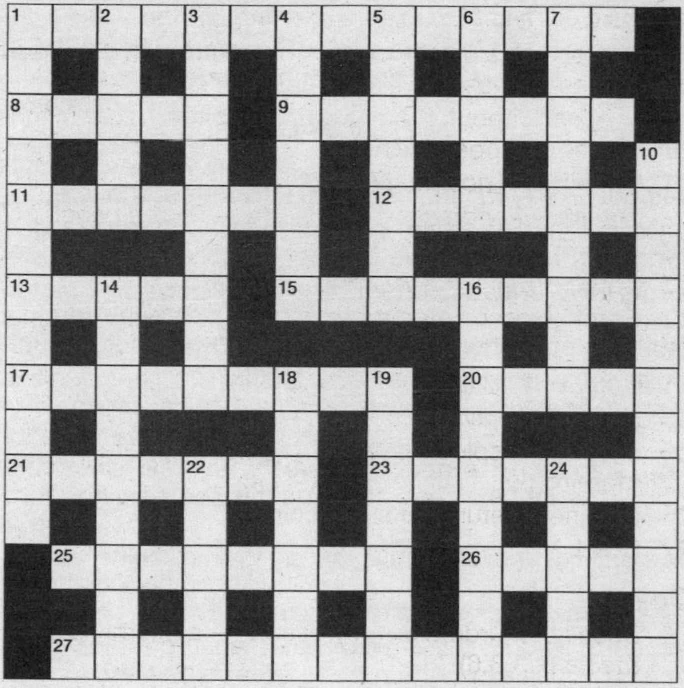

Solve the clues and fit them in where they will go.

A is the next to top line and a lot is interpreted freely (4)

B, one who makes a loud cry, getting model inside campanile (4,5)

C run brigades: with the Spanish, North stand's wrong — include punctuation! (7-11)

D without G are your answer, goes temporis acti laudation (4,2,4)

E is to put up a building in Crete, while refusing to grovel (5)

F, from North Europe, the hero of Trollope's political novel (4)

G could have longed to encourage a silly bird's D reproduction (6,3)

H is a little off colour at heart, caused by vapour or suction (5)

I shall get very cold when it's left in a manner unlawful (9)

J: Knave, Ace, King — that is Jimmie; for Shakespeare's use Ace, Queen, Knave — awful! (5; 6)

K is J's fraud: in American parson reversal will show it (7)

L shows the light that was never on this sea, said (roughly) the poet (6)

M is a painter, one Lawrence, or one in small coins left in heaven (15)

N's just the same, as is one to whom dignity hasn't been given (15)

O come to life into air, for example, when out of alignment (9)

P, it has point in a girl who repeats what is said with refinement (8)

Q with the two leading characters absent or present are arrows (8)

R, when I leave rather red, will be needed to sail through the narrows (6)

S does the car do a five-hundredth part of its journey each second? (7)

T next to A may be X or the lowest in B, it is reckoned (5)

U, Lucy's ways, when in brief, 'ere do shooting and fishing betoken (6)

V, diplomatic reminder that what may be sung may be spoken? (6,4)

W, bellicose bombast appears to have authorisation (7)

X, the unknown getting ready to turn has received radiation (1-5)

Y, which was finished a short time ago, you see swallows sea swallow (11)

Z: here Saul, last and first king, David mourned with reluctance to follow (6)

61

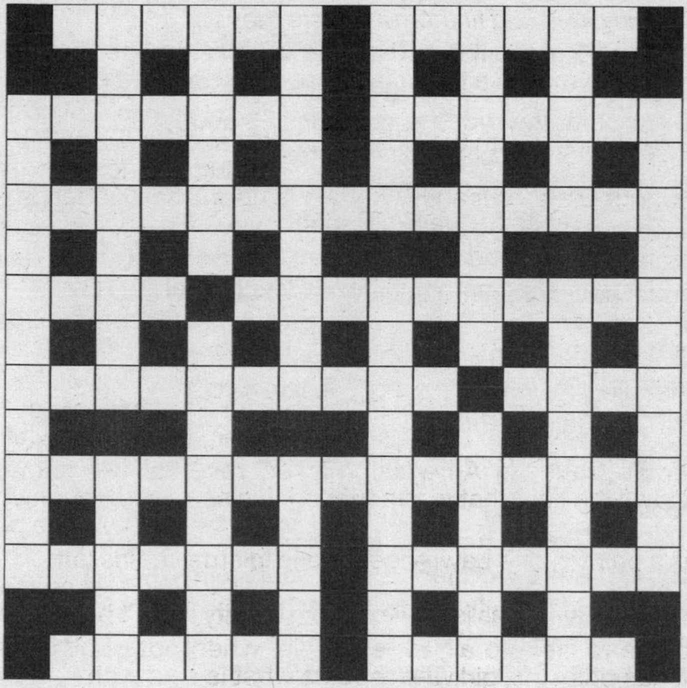

Across

7 Bend in coiffure? (7)
8 Tailless horse-like ungulate in 20 or 24 (7)
10 Apparently it adds and divides 20 and 24 (6)
11 Function of tax on ice — or tax office? (8)
12 Bond's converse costs nothing (4)
13 A rich measure well kept (6,4)
14 Uninspired sort of poetry in a mount (11)
19 Broken sobs among witches mean pirates (10)
22 See 21
23 Unconcealed anger will be exhausting (8)
24 Fall in majority of unmutual backing (6)
25 Girl à la carte? (7)
26 Rhyme on a poster? On the contrary (7)

Down

1 Bird taking a run around in 5 (7)
2 Mad brute produces a sticky sort of rhythm (8)
3 The girl I love turns up — on Clydebank? (3,3)
4 Fairly and old-fashionedly? (8)
5 Westbury is between 24 and 20 (6)
6 Opposed to retreat in defence, which would have sufficed Nelson (7)
9 20 discovered by journalist was justifiable (4-7)
15 Out of work bishop in stone, not much use (8)
16 With the right name? (8)
17 The ways of scurvy varlets? (7)
18 The flaw in the problem is here (7)
20 Rapid rise in tension? (6)
21,22 Don't move! (5,5)

62

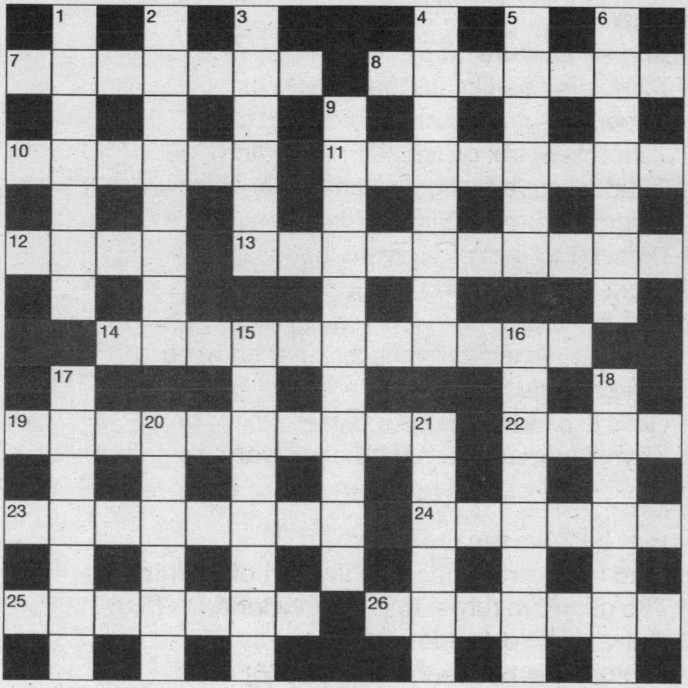

Across

1 Ironed an order of merit in a hurry (7,3,4)
9 They are false in charge (9)
10 Number said in code? (5)
11 Old Bill? That's nice! (5)
12 That missing feeling: attend to the account within (9)
13 Song with one sharp is infectious (8)
14 Braved a storm, in a word (6)
17 How to make ready round the City (6)
19 Lift for endless French scholar on a hill (8)
22 Thought is what makes a sinner go wrong (9)
24 The odd game? (5)
25 One in a feature is sound (5)
26 Tea at four and a change of air makes a cacophony (9)
27 It's posh near the northern part of Edinburgh — company for me, liable to tax (8,6)

Down

1 Sergeant, footsore and torn, has little to pay (10,4)
2 Graceful in a gentle way (7)
3 Whose step goes to the candy store? (5,4)
4 Seaman with American cards — those held (4,4)
5 Revolutionary is a son of a poet (6)
6 Try east and south from the storm (5)
7 Wonder about the car in the distance (7)
8 Kirk official in brewery the worse for drink (10,4)
15 Not a pastime for the main road (9)
16 Protector of the aged? (3,5)
18 The call of a tribe outside Rio (7)
20 Leave out about forty winks, rising at a drum (7)
21 Stone for a Catholic in heaven? (6)
23 Stage work, one side of it at a time (5)

63

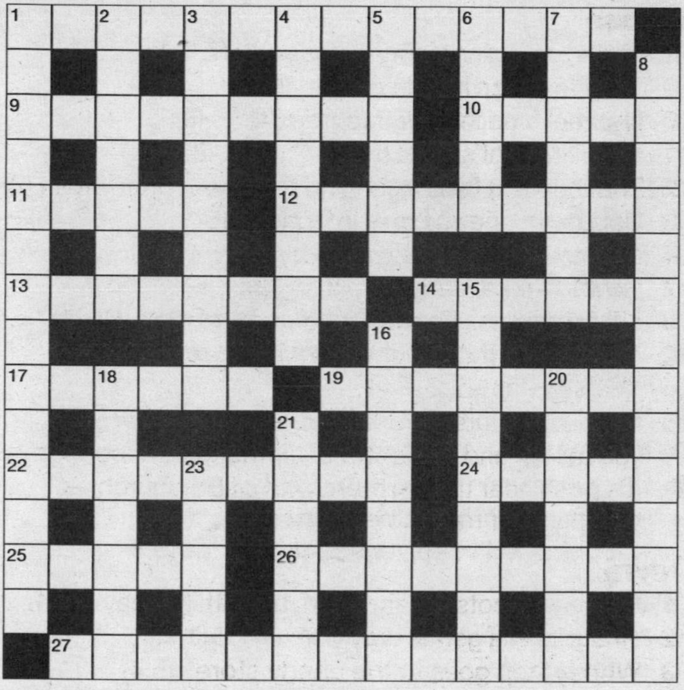

Across

8 It's disgusting here (8)
9 When to go to the 1 (we hear) (6)
10 Poet making merry with a hogshead (6)
11 In this area spasms are unorthodox (8)
12 She returns to feed (4)
13 What can this be? Free grub? (10)
15 They are written backwards by a saint to pious Catholics (7)
16 French dance, a prominent feature to a novelist (7)
18 Digs may be posh, but what's in the tail's repulsive (10)
19 Decay on a 22 (4)
20 Alienate a sergeant? (8)
22 Cock loses nothing in a roll (6)
23 Pull the animal back, Heaven knows! (3,3)
24 The untrained observer seems jealous (5,3)

Down

1 Leader of fashion is, hand on hips, in meat restaurant (4,3,4,4)
2 Ignoble strivers — see them adding 100 to line 500 (3,7,5)
3 They are bad about permits for wills (10)
4 Measure that's French, principally (2,5)
5 A rising force — from 2 for example? (4)
6 Dauphin gives Henry tennis balls, for example (8,7)
7 Book shows pet taking a fruit round in the East (7,2,3,3)
14 Location for rough house's beds? (4,6)
17 Separate a day of victory in a lament (7)
21 The sound of fame (4)

64

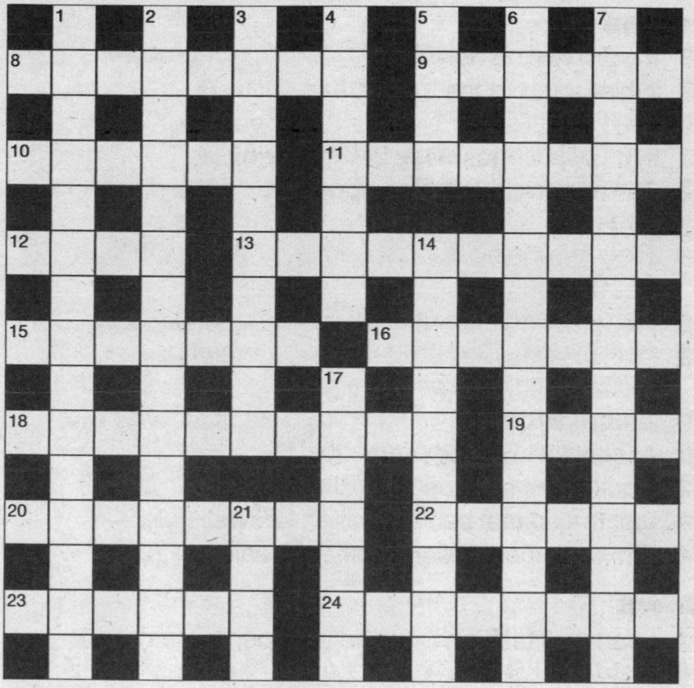

Across

1 Policeman returning with loathing for blue salts (6,8)
9 Scots wear upset the professionals — also ran! (7)
10 Cry for fat (7)
11 A lot of jealousy is bad, they say (5)
12 To say something nice about the crippled can't be bad (9)
13 Elegy's running about half a minute, by the look of it (9)
14 Bard from the first part of Ruddigore (5)
15 Sane? On the contrary, wandering! (5)
17 Skid when the wrong pile's inside (5,4)
20 What's wrong with this spicy man of science? (9)
22 In harbour — near one's goal (5)
23 Pacific literature is nicer, perhaps (7)
24 Summons to fight in a kiosk (4,3)
25 Open or enclosed space? (6,2,6)

Down

1 Castellos (7,2,5)
2 Yield, Fascist! (7)
3 Vermicide (5,4)
4 Weapon for the wall? (7)
5 Books balance on the line (7)
6 Bingo at the Stock Exchange? (5)
7 Still life, perhaps, skilful in character (7)
8 Once white 6 man with nothing on (9,5)
14 Please call Los Angeles a Shakespearean! (9)
16 Mother obeys? Possibly (3,2,2)
17 A little bit of fine weather for the holiday (7)
18 Beguiling fellow to come in about 99 (7)
19 Reached the bottom of the fruit and flower scene (7)
21 I had ten thousand in a manner of speaking (5)

65

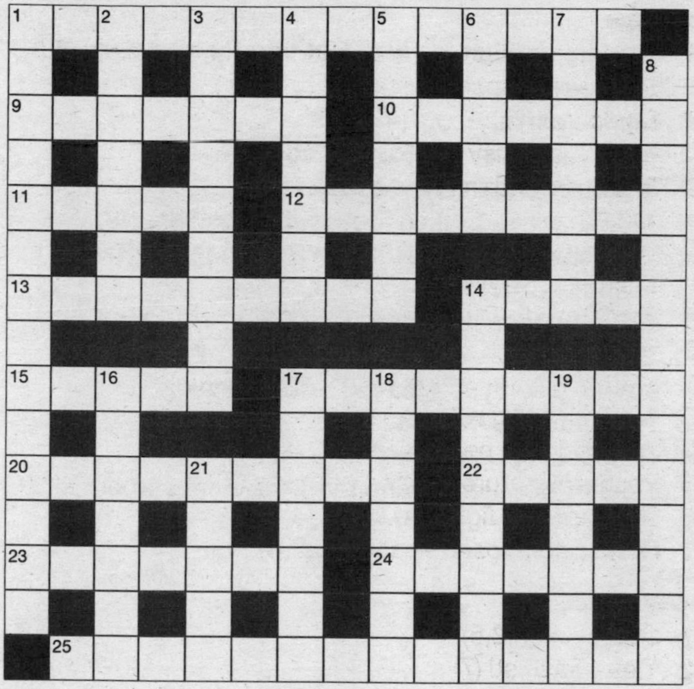

Across

1 PT? In that case one's vocation is the Indian Civil Service (13)
10 Marine constituents (4,5)
11 Man's alternative is to think about love (5)
12 A guru of ancient Rome? (5)
13 African with a broken tooth without shelter (9)
14 "Vanished like a bream" (not Spooner, but Saki) (7)
16 Flying axe? (7)
18 Contender on the waterway? (7)
20 Stop raining — or find a solution? (5,2)
21 I make a song about a high-class vehicle (9)
23 HQ drank backwards (5)
24 Outcast to push off from the rear (5)
25 Poet of New Jersey and made no bones about it (3,6)
26 It's trite to do it with the usual pint (13)

Down

2 Gorilla at odds with crocodile (9)
3 Inferior frown (5)
4 The bag was on the chair by a revolutionary student (7)
5 Dissident cooking the rice (7)
6 Mate or self? (6,3)
7 Superficially small meal (5)
8 A crock, one belonging to a householder, is very tough (2,4,2,5)
9 Characters open for all to see (7,6)
15 Not all that fine, but made the RAF active (4,5)
17 Not French in Paris — universal together (4,5)
19 Cheese on toast, half cooked and half eaten? (7)
20 Can hide the effect of being attached (7)
22 Shock an uppish Northerner (5)
23 Go under personal physician first (5)

66

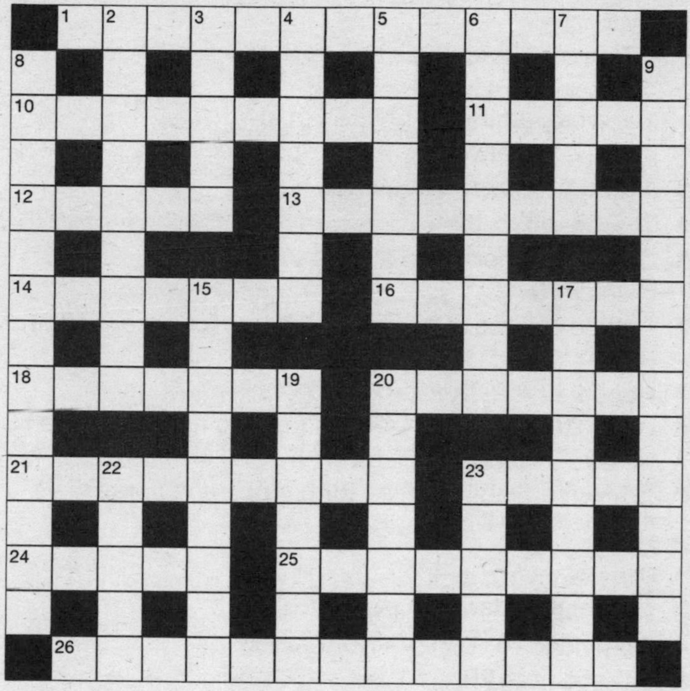

Across

1,5 Death, Sargent's work, is very odd (7,7)
10 Put away for a free ride (4)
11 Train reserve — a little one? (6,4)
12 Access, of course (6)
13 Roedean's odd thought (8)
14 Teacher takes the wrong turn — to see the fur fly? (6,3)
16 Country formed from alkali by acid (5)
17 Clean rotter (5)
19 Fish on a piece of marble, perhaps, for security (5,4)
23 Bird — sound like a dog as well (8)
24 Repeat before the sergeant gets in (6)
26 Where to sleep on a boat — need to turn the lights out (10)
27 It's bad instead of gripping (4)
28,29 Remedy for flatness for cannon and horse (7,7)

Down

2 Girl, about 10, with feeling (7)
3 Drain with a needle? (5)
4 Coming to light on the northern slope (7)
6 Sceptic from Mount Athos (6)
7 Am I a student without brothers? Heavenly! (9)
8 Gerry and Co's shop (7)
9 Complete even if progress is difficult (13)
15 Split up quickly! (9)
18 Try to persuade me to have gunners on the range (7)
20 The bard's coarseness? (7)
21 Boat in a chapter of God's word? (7)
22 Horror writer who feeds the flames (6)
25 Protect the number remaining (5)

67

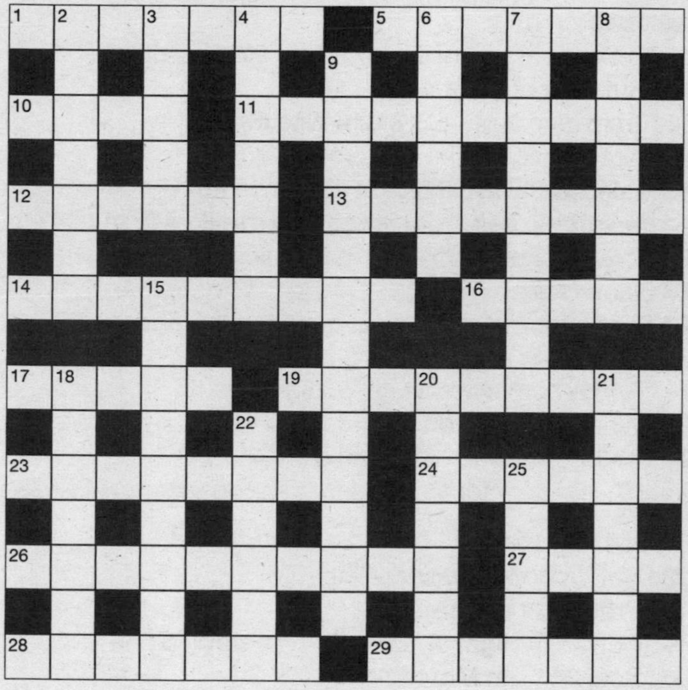

Across

1 You and I at her table mixed gin to keep out the rain (15)
8 Youthful pride? (4,4)
9 Poem by a fool back in Ukraine (6)
10 It links Upton with Lewis (8)
11 Male journalist before an audience (6)
13 Beer at the ball is unpleasant to swallow (6,4)
16 Rotten liar could be falling heavily (10)
19 Sleuth's energy? (6)
20 The bullock at the period provided the cheapest transport (8)
21 Sankey's awfully low-down (6)
22 The obvious things on the ship? (8)
23 Light turner to love in spring (1,5,4,5)

Down

1 Essex all wet then? Wrong — Norfolk! (5-4-3-3)
2 How much for a horse? (6)
3 It rises in anger (6)
4 Traditional teachers about sin in rodents (10)
5 Bird that begins the revolution? (8)
6 One gin is an awful lot for markings (8)
7 End tranquilly and go off pomposo (15)
12 Old transport at the outset gets 2 with rain (5,5)
14 Magician in favour of Latin, I hope! (8)
15 Hide authentications for the family (8)
17 Not to be true (French) to one's creed (6)
18 Local bird with a 5 in it (6)

68

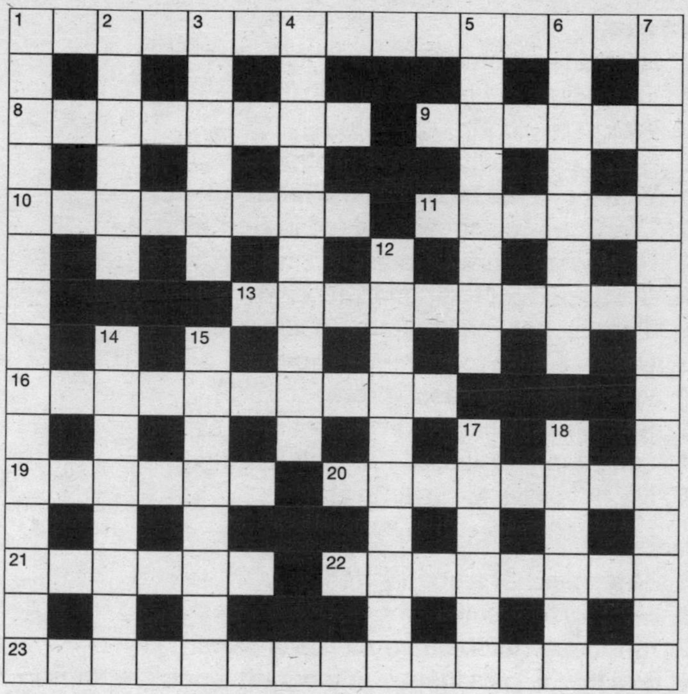

Across

1 Bed at tea time to get publicity? (4-6)
6 Glass upset at tea time: sniff! (6)
9 Wax in a fold (8)
10 School group run on domestic lines? (5,3)
11 Vigilant jester entertains the family (6)
12 Lynn's age discovered of old in Scotland (4,4)
14 He has permission to break silence at one point (8)
16 Attract a Scot to attend Cleopatra (8)
19 Contest between boxers possibly (8)
21 Defence for a roundhead in love (6)
22 What the "antimass" expresses? (8)
23 Something reported from wet mines (4,4)
24 Girl taking in most of you isn't identified (6)
25 My hot cross for St John (10)

Down

1 Garish insect around a tree (6)
2 You louse, we hear, for one (4)
3 Choose what's lighted by novel papers (8)
4 In a hovel, cook naked one naked lunch, perhaps (5,3,6)
5 German town keeps English church in being (7)
7 Standard article across the channel (6)
8 In different ways hides peculiar lingo like Gascon (14)
13 Beast from an Eastern country (5)
15 Words of freedom to returning swimmer (8)
17 Charles's heart's with his beginnings — in Wales (7)
18 Enoch's wrongly elected (6)
20 Obtained meat for wise men (6)
22 Stomach's upset by dirt (4)

69

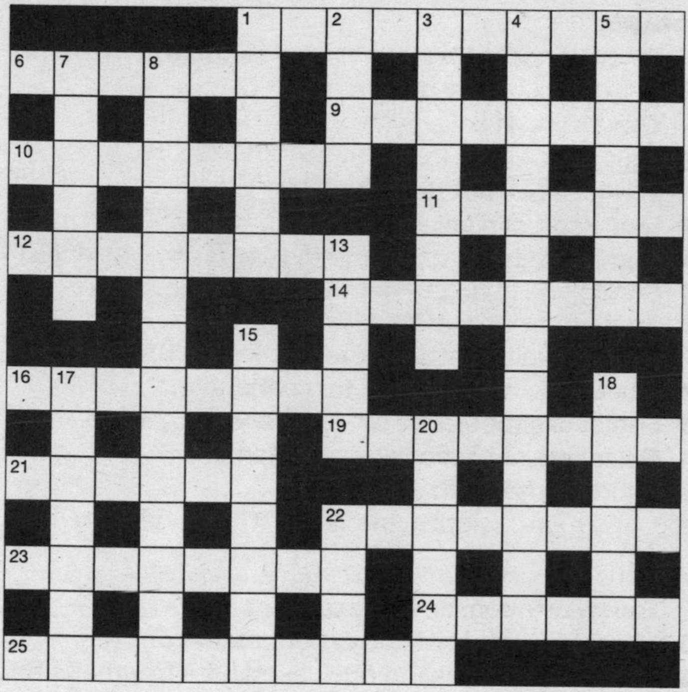

Across

1 Disquiet about lire's spoiled the national anthem (12)
8 Why has the monastery a habit? (7)
9 Clay vessel in college (7)
11 Finished on top? (5,2)
12 Journalist of the RAF's few? (7)
13 Nasty sort of plant (5)
14 Someone else to distribute the cards for Roosevelt (3,6)
16 Something to do with clothes and somewhere to put them — on the line (4,5)
19 In the Middle East's the great lawgiver (5)
21 Diplomatic arrangement for camping in a river (7)
23 Result of exposure of UN submarine by British Navy (7)
24 Designate obligations as questionable (7)
25 Lubricate generously (3,4)
26 Carry more weight in the head? Think again! (12)

Down

1 Fellow with a spice in Alexander's place (7)
2 Humpty-Dumpty's style of condemnation? (7)
3 Illumination struck Eeyore when about to write (3-6)
4 Range of endless destroyer (5)
5 Pacify a fool at the aristocratic period (7)
6 Fun with a silk on a quantity of whisky? (7)
7 Not there and didn't like it! (6-6)
10 Purr is found alone, which one wouldn't expect (12)
15 Sown teeth need a sharpener (9)
17 Month of gold round a future century? (7)
18 Male sergeant at work on a birdcage (7)
19 Person gets sick with a brown envelope (7)
20 Deflationary measure of affection? (7)
22 Being a lot in Germany (5)

70

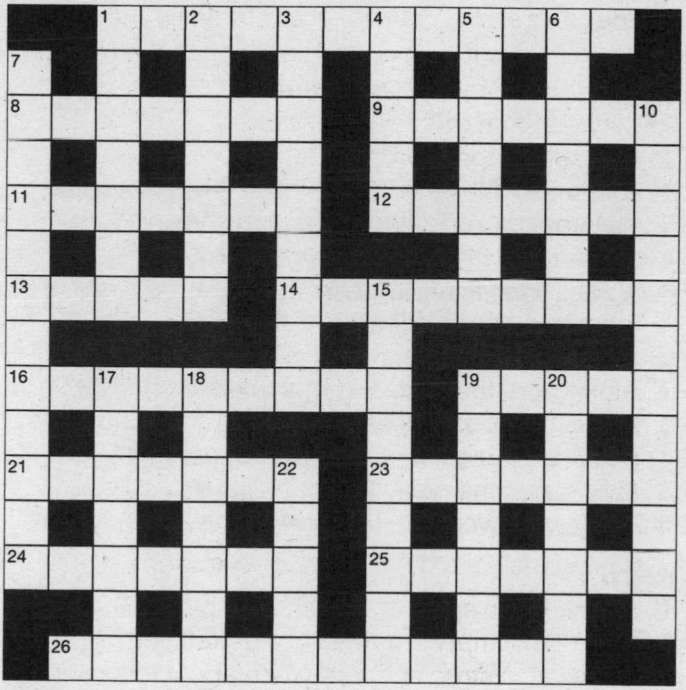

Solve the clues and fit them in where they will go.

A Boy's thus right in, finished with the crowd (4-4)
B African trade unions not allowed? (5)
C Herrings come to healthy flying school (8)
D One with ball at feet is one to drool (8)
E Party problem York's first minster's shown (8)
F Refill ounce? Heir to Bohemian throne? (8)
G Relatively ineffective knot (6)
H Ends in rough, a risky billiards shot (6)
I Headless nomad solvers, it's conceded (1,5,3)
J Hurt, in short, the twelve at trial needed (4)
K Bleaching vat for Hardie, socialist (4)
L Plumbs, in German pop group's vocalist (4,6)
M After sail MC, size zero, unbends (6,6)
N Line between M's rhymes (?) the tender tends (7,5)
O Seeming wise, the bowl is his for keeps (6)
P Tunbridge Wells has resident in heaps (8)
Q To enquire's what's needed — one to enquire (10)
R Criticising parson that's a flier (9)
S Here's two colours — change for pirate John and Bobby: horse too, wry, with nothing on? (6,3,6;8)
T Money's power: a food container (two?) (3,3)
U Short of power, an upset in new blue (6)
V Turn not back: take after form of Eve (4)
W In future Shakespeare has to leave (4)
X Cross fixed for expenses as for debt (1,7)
Y Mat in trifle backward, soured, half set (6)
Z Ox-born fly the devil's part must get (5)

71

Across

1 Not easy money (4,4)

5 Where to drink plenty of sherry wine (6)

9 Spontaneous explosion of gun at hut (8)

10 A poster among film certificates in Coleridge's place (6)

11 Picture, not wholly natural, of plant life? (14)

14 You turn round a joint (5)

15,20 The rough with which to get the smooth? (5,5)

16,17 Scene of 23's 14, kept short among scapegoats (5,5)

20 See 15

22 Encircled at all points with modern soda cups? (9,5)

24 Eleanor at last has her head sculpted, perhaps (6)

25 One who makes the odd record up (8)

26 Get let in with a shilling (6)

27 Tinker about to expound syntax? Not altogether (8)

Down

1 Draw the loot (4)

2 Calder, perhaps: king-emperor with a strange ethic (7)

3,8 Scene of 23's 14, a grave situation for the nation (7,10)

4 "Miss catch" is an order to dissidents (11)

6 Greek spinner's German exclamation interrupts English composer (7)

7 Good man — first class — on the quay (7)

8 See 3

12 Make love, with result a big fall? (4,3,4)

13 Spied trouble: the wire is very low (10)

18 Almost ill after soup with pain in the mouth (7)

19 Most of African 3 in a ship, making 14, perhaps (7)

20 The ploughman in 23's 14 wasn't brilliant (7)

21 Piper takes pain with swagger (7)

23 14 25 on a light note (4)

72

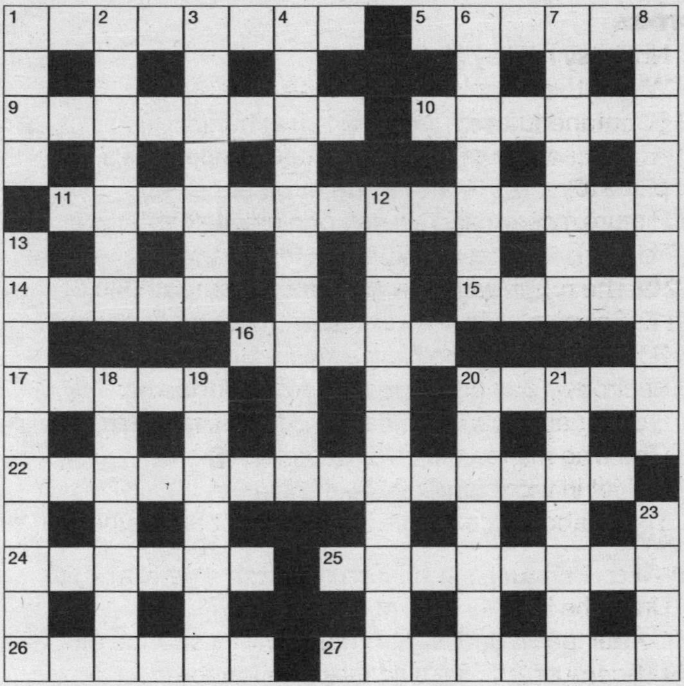

Across

4 Extra time (4,4)
8 A cat in charge of a power? (6)
9 I pretend to be dignified (8)
10 Breakfast out of the fridge, for example (5,3)
11 Breakfast starts with trout, or other fish (6)
12 Revolutionary and Nazi in one piece (8)
13 Use a needle so backwardly to test the town (8)
16 Debts on horses from going by the book? (8)
19 Dandy requests a short visit from a bird (8)
21 Decorated ring the Navy devoured (6)
23 Convey a witch to a point in North Africa (8)
24 Road without a vehicle on it is typically Italian (8)
25 Base by a short head, or swindled (6)
26 Bikes without publicity to the islands (8)

Down

1 Throw about a century on the pitch — that's a bit stiff! (7)
2 Doesn't 'elp and wants more (9)
3 The Southern élite's a yell (6)
4 Darwinian type fount? (6,2,7)
5 Coloured leader? A favourite to have in South Africa (4,4)
6 His money doesn't make him happy (5)
7 Sounds like private spite (7)
14 Liquor in a crock for the pigman (9)
15 Flower bowl? (8)
17 Hoarse? Try a hot collation (7)
18 Profit on the drinks is good business (7)
20 It can be turned by a seraph (6)
22 A covering said to be effective (5)

73

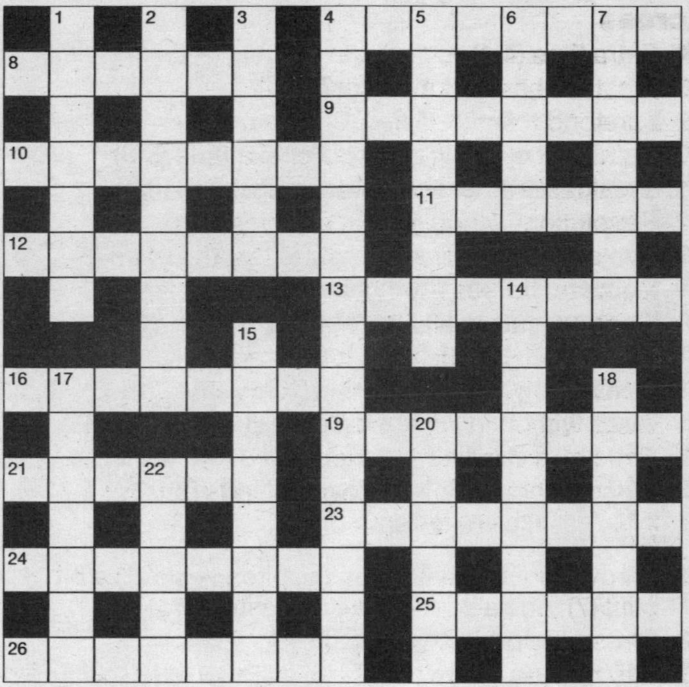

Across

8 Back pound bill to help get weight (8)
9 8 10 gives 6 the right spirit (6)
10 Subscribe (4)
11 Chant scale badly: no hope after this (4,6)
12 8 10, a character from Greece and some from Russia (6)
14 Bring up the majority (8)
15 Messenger from another planet (7)
17 It's crassness to say no sit-in (7)
20 8 10 for a French horn in the Kop (8)
22 8 10 — bow to the lady (6)
23 Complete changes are budding (10)
24 8 10 to attack (4)
25 8 10, for example, turned very small (6)
26 8 10, as in the heresiarch (8)

Down

1 I'm coming back in to give to master (8)
2 8 10 puts up 0 in 0 (4)
3 8 10 on 7 (6)
4 Short dress certain to come to an end (7)
5 Empty cave up where upper class dined (8)
6 Lofty pieces rendered by ignoramus, approximately (5,5)
7 8 10 for science in food (6)
13 Cony gets old bird to bark back a little (4,6)
16 The right hand in it is causing catarrh (8)
18 Huge heat developed in Holland (3,5)
19 8 10 below (anag) (7)
21 8 10's hot line to the North (6)
22 A redhead, stolid, shows enthusiasm (6)
24 Dress the boast up (4)

74

Across

1 A mere quarter for the old PM in Suffolk (10)
8 Female redhead in jug (4)
10 Unorthodox part of mineral aggregate so far (10)
11 Ship's doctor, one may gather (4)
13 Where they used to bait Wyatt, in part (4,3)
15 You have a shilling and about a pound over (6)
16 The cradle of the deep? (3-3)
17 5 down, so to speak, it's so, but it isn't (7,8)
18 Hamlet's "good queen" must have followed the crowd (6)
20 Happy on cake in Suffolk (6)
21 They may confess to being miserable (7)
22 Unusually underdone (4)
25 Leslie in the Brontës' place in Suffolk (10)
26 Repeat of the chorus (4)
27 Beer hall encompassed in Suffolk (10)

Down

2 Bill — he's a pain! (4)
3 Count a listener by his head (4)
4 Knock her this way (6)
5 The range of my narrative possibly recalls Fantasia (2,3,2,1,3,4)
6 Island in the Tweed? (6)
7 Top job for Denys Price? (10)
9 Bowl at a game in Suffolk (10)
12 It sounds a happy town in Suffolk (10)
13 Second class cake in Suffolk (7)
14 Flimsy (not upper class use?) (7)
15 Bad teamwork in a street in Suffolk (10)
19 Render powerless as the Venus de Milo? (6)
20 Feed and read at leisure (6)
23 Cunning sort of spanner (4)
24 Sound of a stream in Wales (4)

75

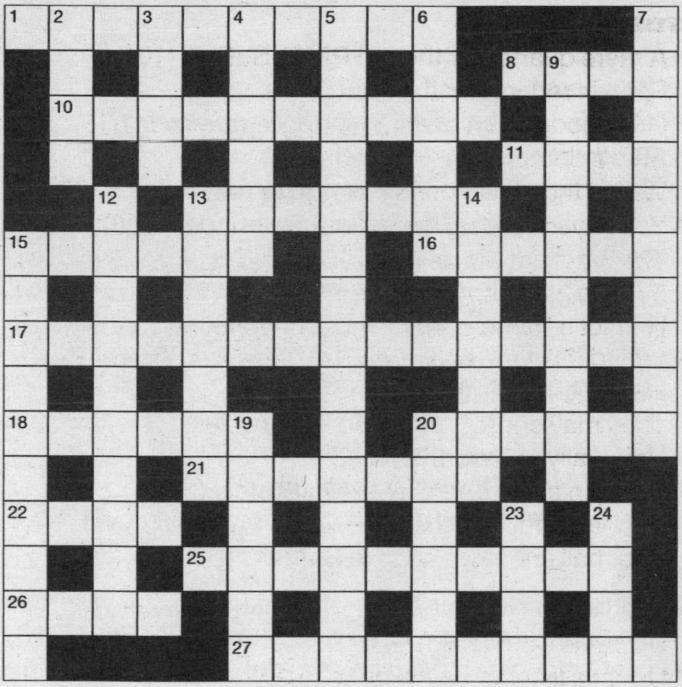

Across

9 Promotion from the architect's point of view (9)
10 24's companion off to sea (5)
11 Centripetal part of a flaming row, no doubt (7)
12 Tend not to be on the level (7)
13 24's companion on Eastern fronts (5)
14 Commander-in-Chief at exposure about sailor in ocean (9)
16 Sounds as if the squire were no newcomer — good acting! (2,3,6,4)
19 Take one's luggage from the rack, but no caps! (5,4)
21 Tribe provided with teeth (5)
22 Parson's back in worship as a channel (7)
23 End of the novel, green if 2 down (7)
24 Great hero of the 14 across! (5)
25 Certainly not, Sir Thomas, as the raven said (9)

Down

1,2,3 Senior NCOs in the matter of the soldier who's crazy are gents out to preserve retreating Other Ranks (10,8,6)
4 I get among people to have a look (4)
5 "Nescient" is rendered as never taking No for an answer (10)
6 Spellman with an apprentice (8)
7 Austere saint gets a bad crit (6)
8 Man from Bisley (4)
14 Man against the Northeast, very hard (10)
15 The second tart could be different (10)
17 Pledges for listener to 22 down spots (8)
18 Love about to sing in a way that isn't pure white (8)
20 24's companion will shortly be with his lad (6)
21 24's companion in shady spots (6)
22 For tea in the snug? (4)
23 Take off the bees? (4)

76

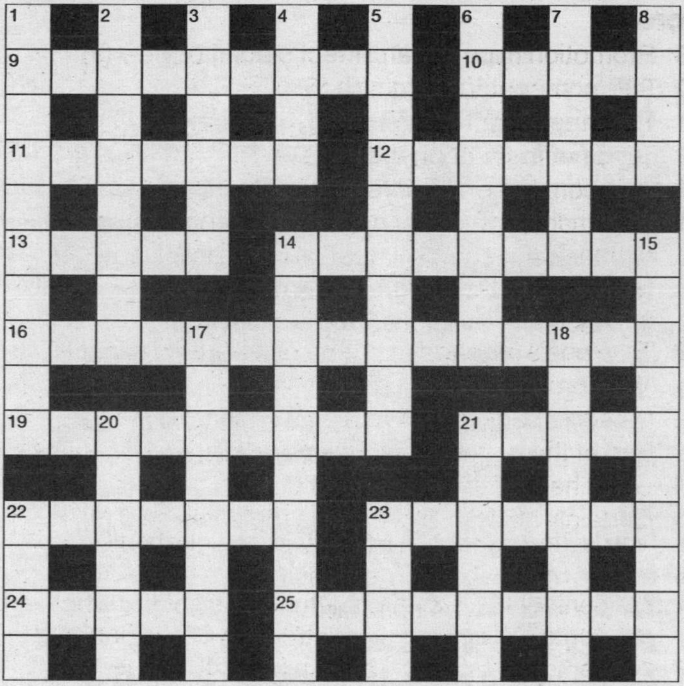

Across

9 Facade of a house? (4,5)
10 Tell, as they say, of fruit (5)
11 Theft of nearly 100? (7)
12 Let off rating and do the puzzle (7)
13,14 Autonomous in personality? (4-10)
16 Advertisement for a pageboy without transport (7)
17 Murderer cut short by quarrel was a low fellow (7)
19 To show round the Spanish is coarse (10)
22,23 Angle cut by kitchen implement (4,5)
24 On Monday morning I get a washing aid (7)
25 Don't let anything go! (7)
26 Alert off? Not yet (5)
27 Hector nun criminally — police may have it in hand (9)

Down

1 One happy school I'll upset with resignation (15)
2 It goes up when it comes down (8)
3 Tender and maybe special (5)
4 Edinburgh's religious area (8)
5 It's a Southern characteristic to be narrow (6)
6 How like St Paul to appear so topical! (9)
7 Ornamental way to come down to others (6)
8 Where's the rhyme? At the terminus? (3,3,2,3,4)
15 The courage of the ladies' man (9)
17 Dismiss at cricket by trickery? (5,3)
18 Primates without leaders around — it means apes (8)
20 Put down a crack in the river (6)
21 It's cunning to call round at the back (6)
23 See 22

77

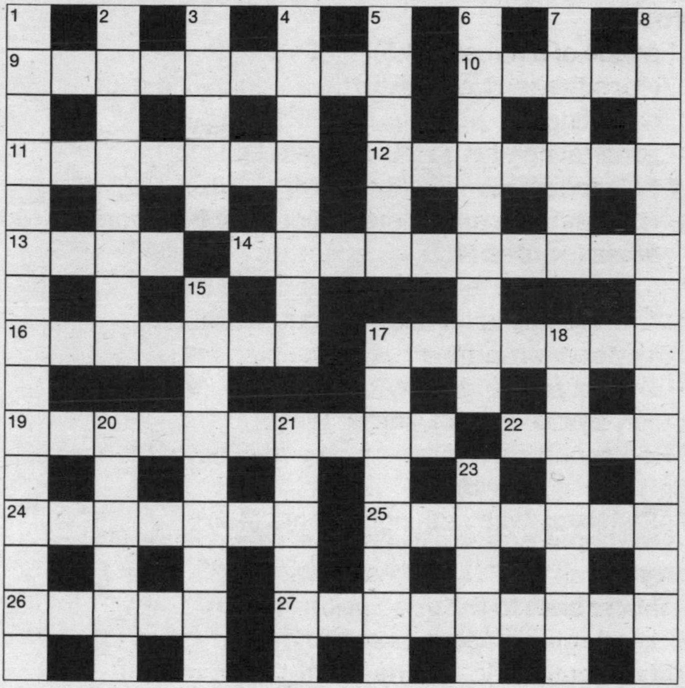

Across

1 Show how to breed (sic)? (8)
5 Our birth, said Wordsworth, is sound if fast (6)
9 Crazy clothes for a student of a song (8)
10 Britain's head in a British symbol (6)
12 Division of Dalmatia (5)
13 Natural 'ealth practitioner about to kill shows how to cross the road (4,5)
14 Psychological error (8,4)
18 Quiet rebellion comes in with initiative (12)
21 The up train? (9)
23 Former Prime Minister often pointed at (5)
24 Happy in a hotel at Edmonton (6)
25 Jew holds on for a short interval (8)
26 Request for 5 (6)
27 Single fair with nothing to spare (4,4)

Down

1 Half points to the conclusion (6)
2 Burden with melancholy and get led astray (6)
3 He's inclined to terrorise (9)
4 Byrd à la Gluck? — that's bad! (12)
6 Like this top? It's substantial (5)
7 Billie, for example, could be qualified (8)
8 Does she let her writing run away with her? (8)
11 Intelligence continues to incite the head cutter (5,7)
15 90-ton transport that doesn't exist (9)
16 Smiles' suggestion for promoting God (4-4)
17 One in the theatre long ago (5,3)
19 Metal work — gold, with a little time and a little luck (6)
20 Menace that's round about (6)
22 A matey affair on board (5)

78

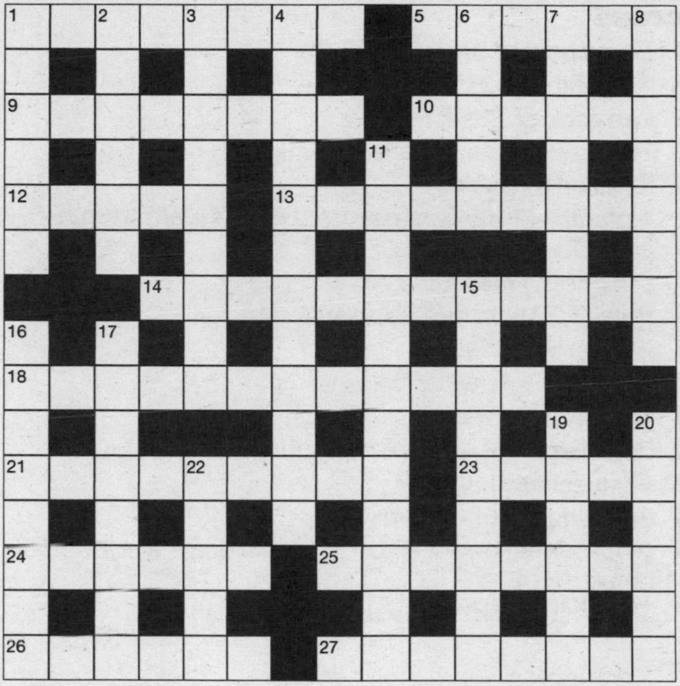

Across

1 Beef counties (8,5)
8 Part of a high school? (5,5)
9 Low form of 25 (4)
11 Footballer (back) for county (almost) has a good memory (8)
12 Worker in Moral Rearmament gets a word from his guru (6)
14 Derby salts? (5)
15 Rate of 20 across's ebb (5)
16 Gun for a soldier (5)
17 Teach the following (5)
20 Too much for a canoe? (5)
22 Engineers' subsidies for monarchies? (6)
23 Afflict as barbers do? (8)
25 Agreement from 19 (4)
26 A policeman and a witch in Indian dress are funereal objects (10)
27 The East Berlin sphere may be to blame (13)

Down

1 One of nine men, a sailor and a rebel, over the pintables (9,6)
2 Ruler returns me the papers (7)
3 It's crazy round here up in Norfolk (7)
4 Nero and two lads for Leeds United (6,4)
5 ... ran unsuccessfully (4)
6 Revealed secret about quiet ghost (7)
7 Family car to let: eats inside a 1 across sandwich once found in Grampian region (15)
10 The land of 5 (4)
13 Figure of Eastern clericism? (10)
18 A friend to an old city, unpaid (7)
19 Title for 24 (4)
20 The creature has a month at work (7)
21 Favourite little woolly jumper (3-4)
24 9 turns on the lion (4)

79

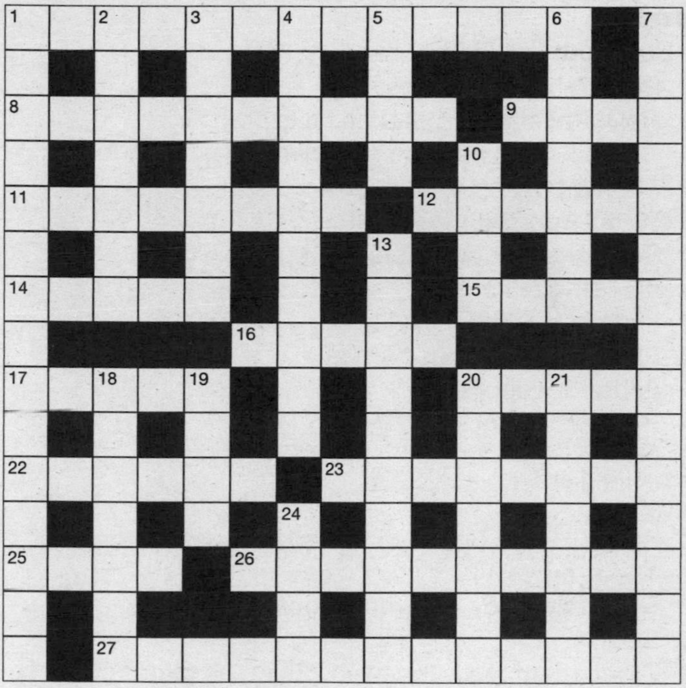

Across

7 Tether to the French tree (5)
8 Penetrative in charges? (9)
9 Hair in poetic surroundings has point (5)
10 Comedy gets the staff on strike (9)
12 Made up 22? (7,4)
16,21 22 from 3 (9)
17 Small mark about 4: please replace it (5)
18 It's taken seriously (4)
19 22 to engulf the end (11)
22 Fat, crafty, frivolous type (9)
24 Looter's weapon? (5)
25 5 22? 21 or brick? (5,4)
26 Is she a spinster? (5)

Down

1 Ship pictured by a river — it's between Worcs. and Yorks. rivers (9)
2 Heavenly study with many roots (9)
3 See 14
4 Dior patient, perhaps, with 22s in the stomach? (11)
5 Cabbage 22, a blow among opposites (5)
6 Saint sends one back to church (5)
11 22 — field looking parched (6-5)
13 The honest are on it (5)
14,3 22 moving house? (13)
15 Boy (page 51) in attachment (9)
20 Society forded in Surrey (5)
21 See 16
23 "To (sound of) 20 refined gold, to (start of) 12 the _____." (King John) (4)

80

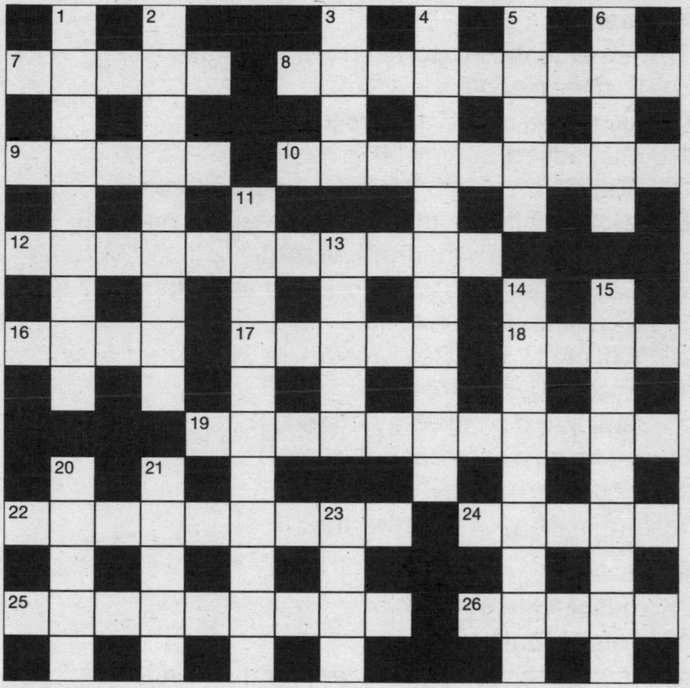

Across

1 Means of ascent (spelt wrong) by snake (10)
8 Burn the cleaner's tea? (4)
10 Had made, say, 101 per cent? (10)
11 Unidentified, shortly (4)
13 Loud cry on rough ground next the church (7)
15 Psychic about an officer in the feudal system (6)
16 It's stupid to love a drunkard (6)
17 Illuminati put youngster on a plane to Reno (8,2,5)
18 Ring that is written to? (6)
20 Walk of the Holy Rollers? (6)
21 It's gone by due to neglect (7)
22 Censor and scrutinise nothing (4)
25 The recep. Hitler was after? (6,4)
26 Altogether? (4)
27 Turn of king to break pitcher? (6,4)

Down

2 Kind of writing (4)
3 Protrude quietly out (4)
4 Means of becoming, in New York, 100 years old? (6)
5 Mathematical process undergone by distinguished people? (15)
6 Fabulous bird may somehow coo in style (6)
7 Public mansion? (5,5)
9 County fellow in the pink? (10)
12 A grave diet for the motley (10)
13 Did academic work, which isn't natural (7)
14 Has, we hear, literary associations (7)
15 Contemplate thrift to maintain dignity? (4-6)
19 The hills have to 22 it (6)
20 "South with Berry" is the catchword (6)
23 Game to beat up (4)
24 Ruler in the mire (4)

81

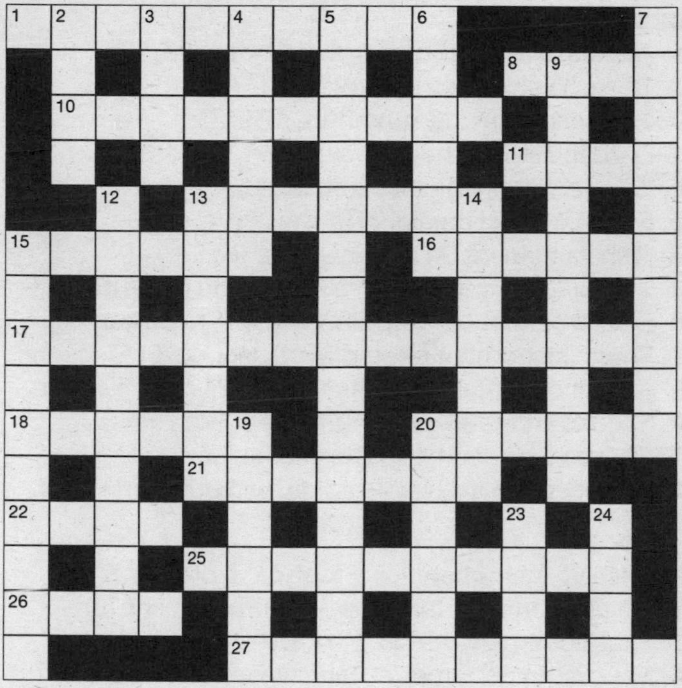

Across

4 Like the Floral dance band of Linden? (8)
8 Tenor, a vehicle, as above, for the Ring (6)
9 Nuts were used as substitute milk (3,5)
10 Debilitated, like the police station, endlessly (8)
11 Wander, within reason, by boat (6)
12 Signifies "read music"? (8)
13 Fifth instrument on a hill near Venice (8)
16 Third instrument, one for a king in the grave (8)
19 Background for toothbrush, maybe, to be kept stiff (5,3)
21 Fourth instrument often played second (6)
23 Flatten pretentiousness in Cromwellian fashion (8)
24 Second instrument, fashionable in wine (8)
25 Chase us back among the chaste (6)
26 It's very good that Leonard did without children (8)

Down

1 Seventh instrument for a fool in the present (7)
2 Ninth instrument turns up — I hum with one (9)
3 First instrument was in the cavalry (6)
4 Magpies in St James's Park, wasn't it? Need clue? NE FC (9,6)
5 Silence! It's inadmissable in Scrabble! (3,1,4)
6 Eighth instrument, a loud one (5)
7 Most of the balustrade's left for purifying (7)
14 Little Emily's badge of servitude, no doubt, by the door (9)
15 Without the pioneer of sci-fi, Divinity was in control (8)
17 Not quite a ruin, just a small mistake, near London (7)
18 Sixth instrument, with a bit of 1 in it, for bird with mug (3,4)
20 The side that doesn't delay? (6)
22 Lament, for example, delivered upside down (5)

82

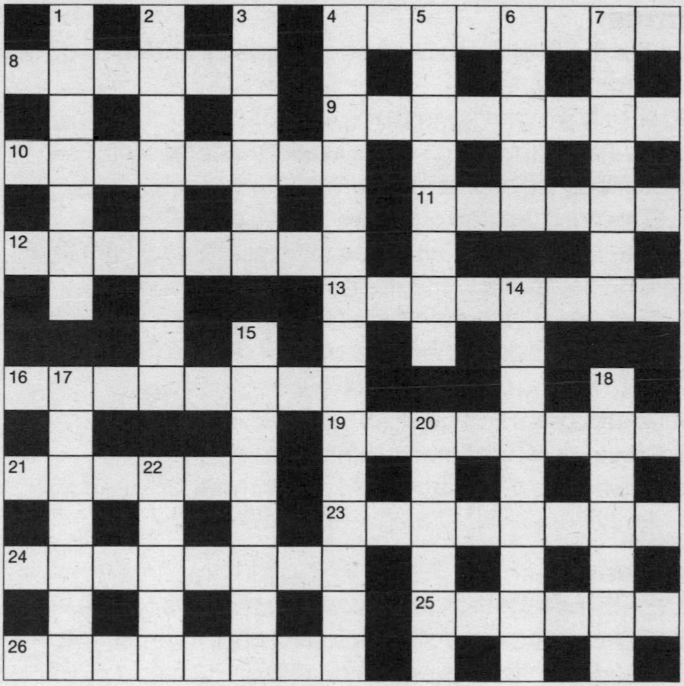

Across

1 The leaders perish and people start slandering down under (3,7,4)
9 It's right in colour in a dog (3-3-3)
10 By the willow he must be in the water (5)
11 Circuits point to a fall (5)
12 The creature has globality, perhaps (5,4)
13 The octopus has what ten can't quite deal with (8)
14 Dog set for heavy stuff (6)
17 See what Catherine's said to find (6)
19 Boat capsized when bird got in in Africa (8)
22 Talk a lot to get Pete a taxi (9)
24 A mongrel? Not quite (5)
25 No. 99's returned issue (5)
26 Plain type of fish stick (9)
27 Leave not without a fight and be 3? (3,3,3,5)

Down

1 Baby Elizabeth, hardly anything besides (4,6,4)
2 It gets knocked down for less than a florin at home (7)
3 Anti interchanges on the road (9)
4 It preserves a fairy at a dance (8)
5 Shakespearean relation, a sister — Cleopatra's part (6)
6 Room for politics (5)
7 A lucky shot in the North of France etc (3-4)
8 Understand how to put up a picture? (3,3,4,2,2)
15 Sat up at the parsonage, a setting for 1 across (6,3)
16 The snowshoe in my all-French velvet (8)
18 Officer I have taken prisoner (7)
20 Pear returns a number of eggs with trouble (7)
21 To preserve one's preserves, traffic a lot of cannabis (3,3)
23 A dance makes the sunburn wear off (5)

83

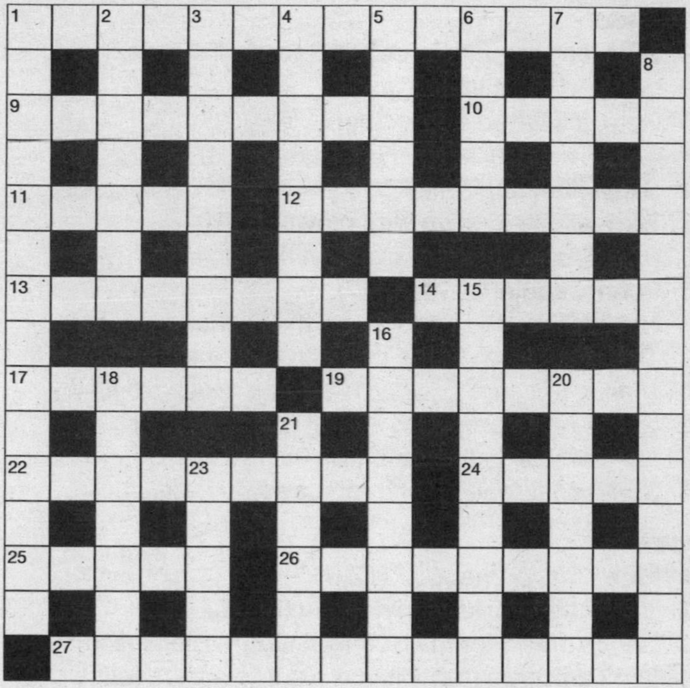

Across

8 Where to catch the flea? (2,3,3)
9 Leave in West Indian style? (2,4)
10 Here, if wanted, is the animal (6)
11 Actors aplenty leave it to chance (4,4)
12 Bill of fare for gentlemen? (4)
13 Turn off one in town with clowning (10)
15 Paper runners rot inside from right to left (7)
16 Scent acquired by rage (7)
18 Not prepared to endure into the French oratory (10)
19 The end of the road is the start to the setter (4)
20 "False, fleeting, ______ Clarence" (Richard III) (8)
22 Couple in appropriate vessel get busy (2,4)
23 I'm doing all I can to include the French (6)
24 Shakespearean royal family, awfully regal (4,4)

Down

1 Free time, perhaps … (12,3)
2 … for the quarter, a joyful result (3,6,2,4)
3 Hero's brand for the beetle in Gray's Elegy (5-5)
4 Look around the city if you want to particularise (7)
5 A long time for a gesture (4)
6 Stones and bread? All right for a brief encounter (4,3,8)
7 "So, Mr Latimer! – Mary" (anag) (7,8)
14 Clear water falling gets stale, probably (10)
17 Beard for 5 and the wrong key (7)
21 The unmoved mover – of 5 maybe (4)

84

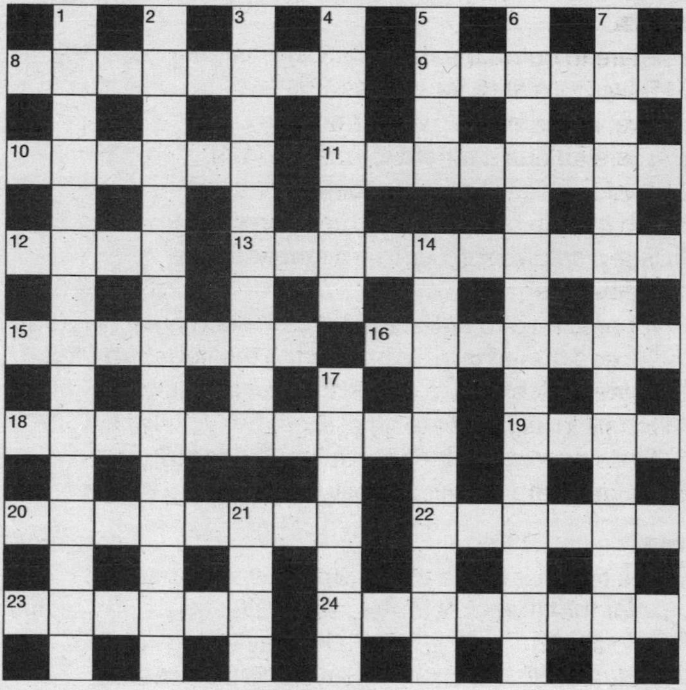

Across

1 Appearances of humanity, if at Eastern posts (14)
9 Descent is time for a row (7)
10 Exeunt the barbarian, for entering (2,5)
11 The eyot has a tenant (5)
12 A vet with a kilt may be loquacious (9)
13 Wound the senior at the fuel store (9)
14 See a soldier start coming to reason (5)
15 Trees determined by tests (5)
17 A pressing affair? Remains to be seen (5,4)
20 Glory diffused in welcome is the religious aim (4,5)
22 Hard work by rose growers, for example (5)
23 Score a goal a game (7)
24 One who establishes the second adage? (7)
25 Be bold and risk getting stung (5,3,6)

Down

1 In Pooh's author a champion at sonic speed gets attached to a cow (7,7)
2 Minus? (7)
3 Irritable German women, about ten carat (9)
4 Labour can be satisfied if we get in (7)
5 Not straight and not curved (7)
6 Ran if in trouble — see below (5)
7 Kind of home that makes railwaymen give tongue (7)
8 The principal painter of the county? (5,9)
14 A student I am, for example, and wander — to the orchard? (4,5)
16 Composer with hesitation takes a gun (7)
17 Little old wound? It's red (7)
18 Figure of 1¼ yards itself (Latin) (7)
19 About time to hire a chemical (7)
21 Forecaster one can see through (5)

85

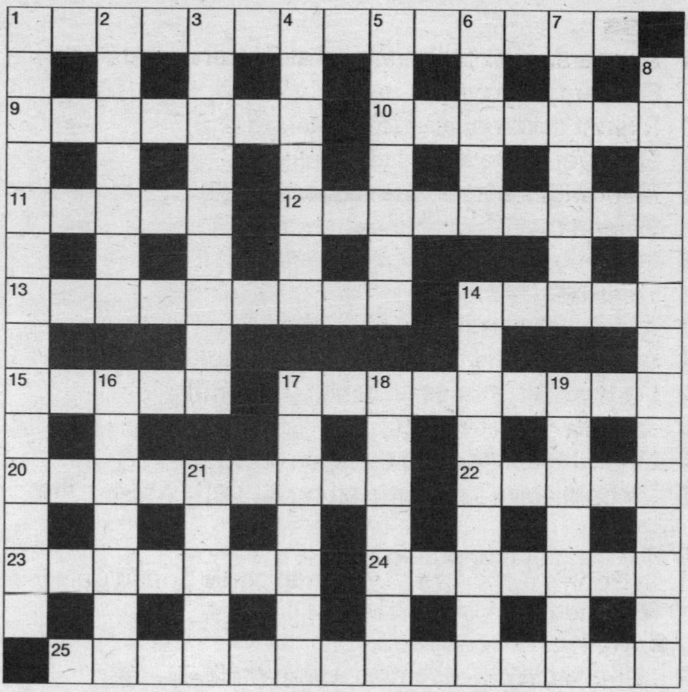

Across

1 Maybe Wordsworth's too modest about the Spanish (7)
5 For company the custom is to live together (7)
9 Blake's bright burner (5)
10 Glad it's not serious, in fact (9)
11 Meritorious person's understanding about Ivor eating everything (10)
12 The little beast will be a flatterer (4)
14 Pas pas? (11)
18 7 by a wrong note? (6,5)
21 Assistant's bad idea (4)
22 Change into a dove and capsize? (4,6)
25 Trip after 1 across? (9)
26 Legal case associated with error (5)
27 Thanks, there's nothing in the concert: where's the beer? (7)
28 Try hand at firefighting? (7)

Down

1,2 No leg broken in apostolic motor (6,6)
3 Still a virgin? Invade with a rush? (10)
4 Always includes the instincts to duck (5)
5 Vivid demonstration of Lulu for CO (9)
6 Victor's embrace with love (4)
7 Given away bread yet? (8)
8 Good order requires one row in a novel (8)
13 Nut and date tea could be long drawn out (10)
15 Four fume terribly about flu caused by decaying matter (9)
16 "Dad" turns to "Dad or Mum", as it seems (8)
17 It sounds like useful headgear for golfing status (8)
19 Turn tail at the barbarian invader (6)
20 The favourite's about a length in the lead (6)
23 Choral extract from "The Man in the Iron Mask" (5)
24 So the giant's back (4)

86

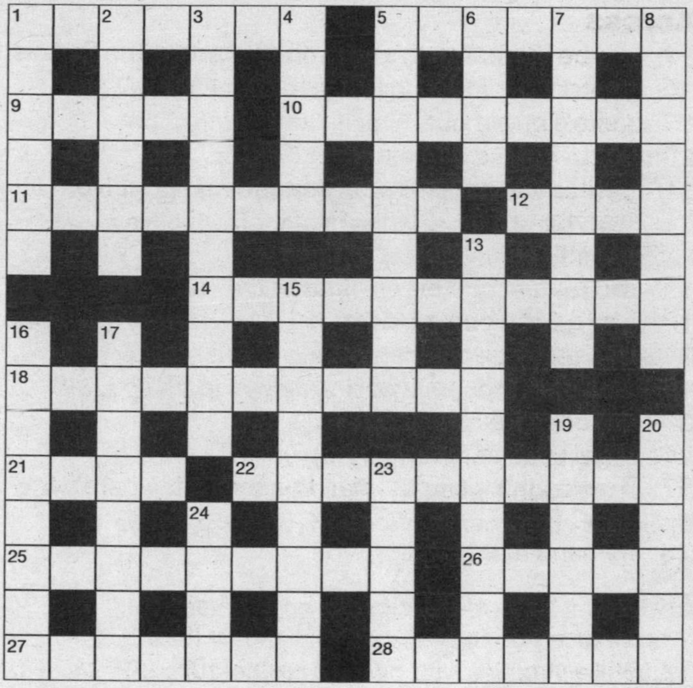

Across

1 Film man creates company on jet spirit (13)
10 Immobilise something liable to injury (9)
11 Decoration without drink is little comfort (5)
12 It is not without interest (5)
13 Fruit tree with fruit (9)
14 Brown bit of Scots capital transferred to New Zealand? (7)
16 Word to describe pie cooked at the Turk's Head (7)
18 Red rose put behind the altar (7)
20 Some folks tell a romantic tale about stars (7)
21 Company for captain of double-rigged ship? (3-6)
23 Where to hide money? (5)
24 An eye to an ear is anear! (5)
25 Let and don't let go — could be all he does (9)
26 Social or financial difficulty? (13)

Down

2 Subject for investigation by coastguards or stewards? (3-6)
3 Jollyboat starts with painter on the quay (5)
4 Murderer of the century (epitaph by writer) (7)
5 Young thing with upper-class engine? (7)
6 Fruit of internecine blacking (9)
7 Bad housing on the quiet causes depression (5)
8 Support for garment should at first knock (8,5)
9 Toast despatched on Friday in the evening's in Berlin (6,7)
15 Did the wicked landlord not complete the Greeks' old money? (9)
17 Does old English money mean divided rule? (4-5)
19 Colonist who pays his bills? (7)
20 Cries of 23 down in the ship (7)
22 First piece of music — ditto backwards — from Poppy (5)
23 The best hundred and twenty quires (5)

87

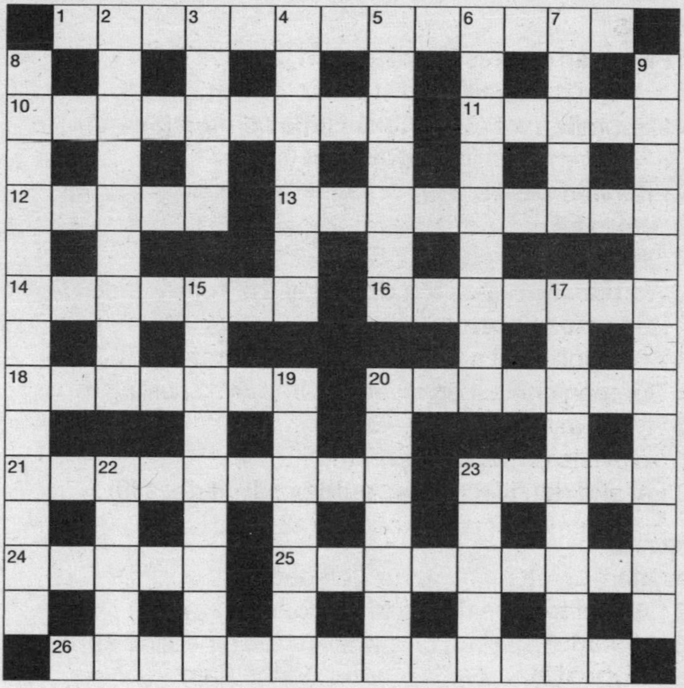

Across

1 Dance instruments (8)
5 The vice-captain's a bit chilly (6)
9 Security man gets a bad name on transport (3-5)
10 Gloomy but mild as possible (6)
12 Dance to make sunburn disappear (5)
13 + 44 (4,5)
14 Insect on the grass (7,5)
18 Is Titania cruel to the dumb? (12)
21 Revenge on ahead? (3,3,3)
23 Poet, novelist and priest (Old Testament) (5)
24 Getting oneself up in a costume that's wrong (6)
25 It shows (8)
26 That's said to be wide and blue (6)
27 Ass cured by runners, as they say (4,4)

Down

1 Non-Aryan meat, an unfinished item (6)
2 Animal's lair in decay (6)
3 Underworld king, criminal leader, renegade and tycoon (9)
4 Intelligence shown by a southern type town (12)
6 Leader of a church that's feminine (5)
7 Reckoner's arrival placed within (8)
8 Defensive help for royal house, we hear (8)
11 The very words! (12)
15 Stupid Dad, having lost his tail, may be dead (3-6)
16 I try with less effect, relatively speaking (8)
17 Quiet worker, but prejudiced (8)
19 5 and 9 ruined a capital (6)
20 This beat is a strain (6)
22 Lightweight carnivore (5)

88

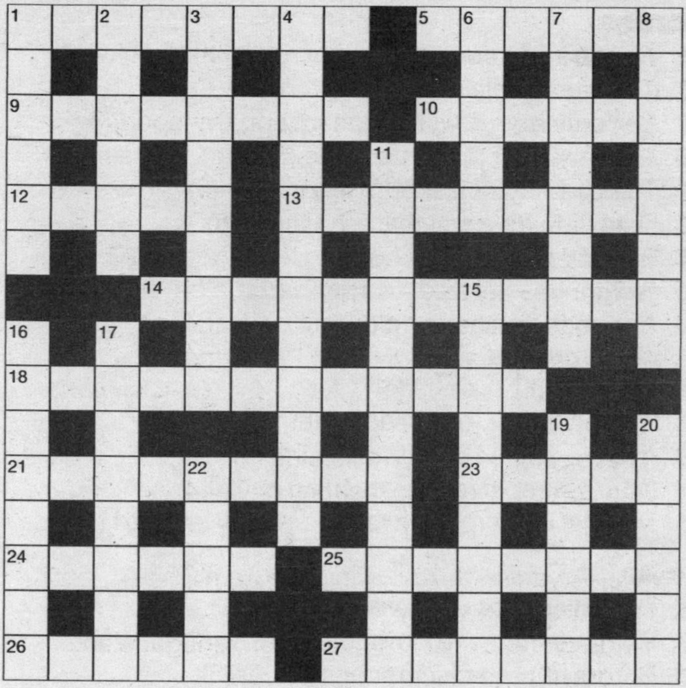

Across

1 Whence one comes to caper round the cooker (10)
6 It points to cold ground (6)
9 Being flirtatious with plugs? (8)
10 Administrator puts poster project before insect (8)
11 Strangely coincidental, club 99! (6)
12 Occasion for a suit that isn't there (8)
14 Political belief that is nothing if not godly? (8)
16 Weight desiderated "in summertime on Bredon?" (4-4)
19 About, for example, to inform on a chosen representative (8)
21 Wicket left by fellers (6)
22 Scraps about "demn dots" (8)
23 Avoid a course of Marxian screening (4,4)
24 Course that gives points to an actor (6)
25 Musical instrument in ranch built by law lord (10)

Down

1 Prated about explosive (6)
2 Remove from one's moustache (4)
3 Return of cutter, digger and tester (8)
4 Confession or thanksgiving? (14)
5 Tower of trickery? (7)
7 Grub about on Ethiopian capital (6)
8 Peasant wins Kintbury Cup on M (7,7)
13 Give up the harvest (5)
15 "One foot in ______ and one on _______" (Much Ado) (8)
17 'Ave a look for a girl? That's a lie! (7)
18 Representation of a girl without vulgar ornamentation (6)
20 Pupil with a snake that's not a snake (6)
22 Friend with ring of stone (4)

89

Solve the clues and fit them in where they will go.

A's a diabetic,nearly; heat is not transferred (9)
B, boy's name, title to house, shown briefly: see seabird! (11)

C, boy's name, read Stanley Prong: he ruled with ball and bat (11)
D depicted guys and dolls: mum's on the run — that's that! (5,6)

E, boy's name, a shortened form that's vortiginous (4)
F,boy's name, upsets the umpire, then there's uproar plus! (9)

G's unfinished sporting contest — master makes a ray (5)
H, six-sided jinx, an anagram of a long A (9)

I, boy's name of old, a saint: seems Bob belongs to me (4)
J, boy's name, card, flag, or fish, lifts car or goes to sea (4)

K, when part of Brighton's lost its own, had rare good comb (5)
L, boy's name, when shortened, leading railway guard at home (5)

M, boy's name, at Minehead will prepare a peer to fight (9)
N's the first of Northern districts: not a soul in sight! (4)

O for lovebirds, stupid things! (Unusual form of word) (5)
P, boy's name, may topple peer and reign with foreign bird (9)

Q, boy's name in short, an organ stop or fiddle string (5)
R returns the lager that is worthy of a king (5)

S, boy's name — Jerusalem round last of Abraham (5)
T, boy's name in Latin form: skip back to Uncle Sam (9)

U, for Ben (not Scots) in Irish blue, freed Africans (5)
V, boy's name, a fast in tree: loveletter, unknown man's (9)

W, or sword woke changes: plane and saw they use (11)
X, gray phlox to change impression made by W's (9)

Y, round-mountain-singing youth with love and peace in mind (5)
Z, the last, last first, had Ruritanian king confined (5)

90

Across

1 Depressing and depressed — and bruised (5,3,4)
8 Sergeant at heart, maybe, in spite of sounding like a private (7)
9 Marigold can take a large size drink (7)
11 Enthusiastic for a love beginning in the heart of God (7)
12 Could ye convert the Scots, kindly? (7)
13 11, perhaps, with small fish about, that is (5)
14 Musical openings made diplomatically (9)
16 Bird with yellow 21 (9)
19 What is the explanation of that? (5)
21 High speed ahead? (7)
23 Free with a capital T? (2,5)
24 Engagement broken? Stop phoning! (4,3)
25 Substratosphere for vanishing? (4,3)
26 Tool for primate's painful parting? (6-6)

Down

1 Slavery — when people read Ian Fleming (7)
2 Sorry sort of defence? (7)
3 Been stork (that's wrong!) by the road (9)
4 Man as ape? (5)
5 Veto on quiet: I leave the feast (7)
6 Dubious and largely relative (7)
7 Value a combat aircraft highly? (12)
10 Tax system for the AA, a syrupy one? (3,2,3,4)
15 It gets out more carat gold (9)
17 Lion about to breathe heavily in battle (7)
18 Chase a bird round a girl (7)
19 One hill for a fiend (7)
20 Twist a twisted hat in the way to battle (7)
22 Welshman, very loud, in Scots river (5)

91

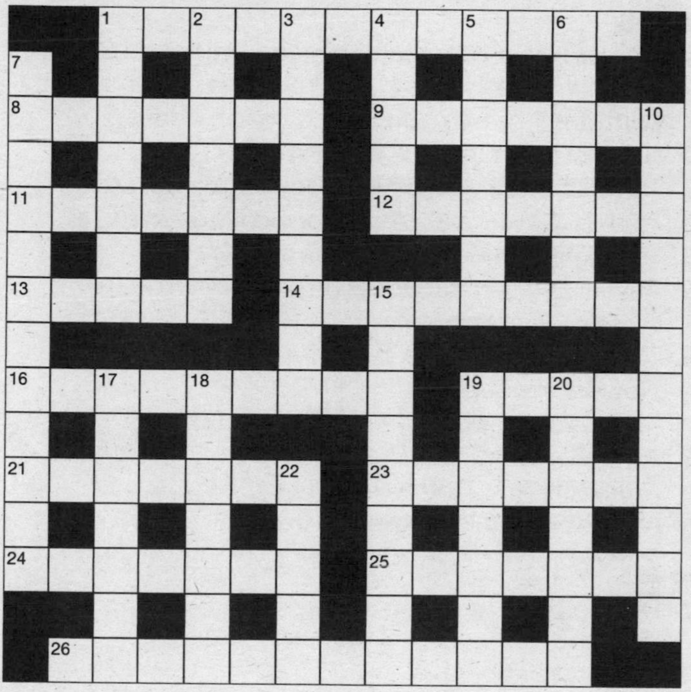

Across

1 First ordeal: the quenching of the sacred flame? (7,2,4)
9 Send another way about, out, inside, about (2-5)
10 Novelist returning sick at heart (7)
11 Traveller in biology, psychology etc (5)
12 Trouble in Worcestershire's back: it's alarming (9)
13 The eighth prune stone or tea leaf (5)
15 Animal and vegetable will be productive (4,5)
17 Druid seen from below (9)
18 The land of France re-taken? Not yet (5)
19 Flower for weed? (9)
22 Decimals can do it again and again (5)
23 Away from land, points to the prize (7)
24 Article on 18 in Rome (7)
25 Last to be drunk, single, will travel (3,3,3,4)

Down

2 Dip the oar — it will break, owing to long disuse (9)
3 I am yours (5)
4 Poet cut short by sailor in ballad (5)
5 Smithy with German air rises oblivious (9)
6 The boss will get things straight (5)
7 Terrorism keeps the rest shuffling (13)
8 Salt Lake's river and university (13)
10 The acting had developed with care (7)
14 It separates the toss from the break (5,4)
15 Pirate found by FBI man in chateau? (7)
16 Rash old city gets convulsion with song (9)
20 The links are a prominent feature outside (5)
21 God gives everyone satisfaction (5)
22 It goes round either way (5)

92

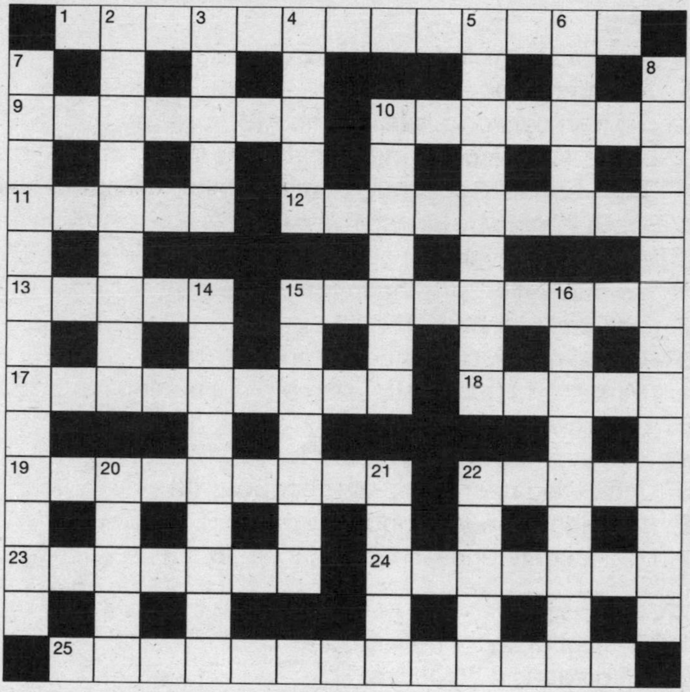

Across

1 Jester's Morris incomplete 16 (8)
5 Very funny noise? (6)
9 The turn ours give is lamentable (8)
10 Threaten a mischief-maker's demise (6)
11 Chief redcap, Scots mayor, and ceremonial authority (7,7)
14 South African by birth (5)
15 Masque of revelry (5)
16 Salvationist gets round in the pair (5)
17 Potential potential? (5)
20 Roman meeting, refined in appearance (5)
22 Dumas eats Dumas, causing representations to be made (6,8)
24 They swallow gold on paper (6)
25 Unfinished decree in plain chiropody (8)
26 Bertrand sounds sound! (6)
27 Made a difference to the insincere (8)

Down

1,23 A lot of liquor may include tusks (8)
2 I'm great as a detective (7)
3 New life for a parson and four others (7)
4 Suppress those around a monarch in place of a game (6,5)
6 Two thirds of a university, approximately, are material (7)
7 Whence the first woman by pretence got the fruit? (7)
8 Decoration, we hear, with which a few are interfering (10)
12 Male to inform about female (feminine) over the fire (11)
13 Air force gauge with remote name (10)
18 Heathen depart penniless! (7)
19 Belt with rim bent by an old instrument (7)
20 Breakable record about scrap of cloth (7)
21 Secure point about lack of faith (7)
23 See 1 down

93

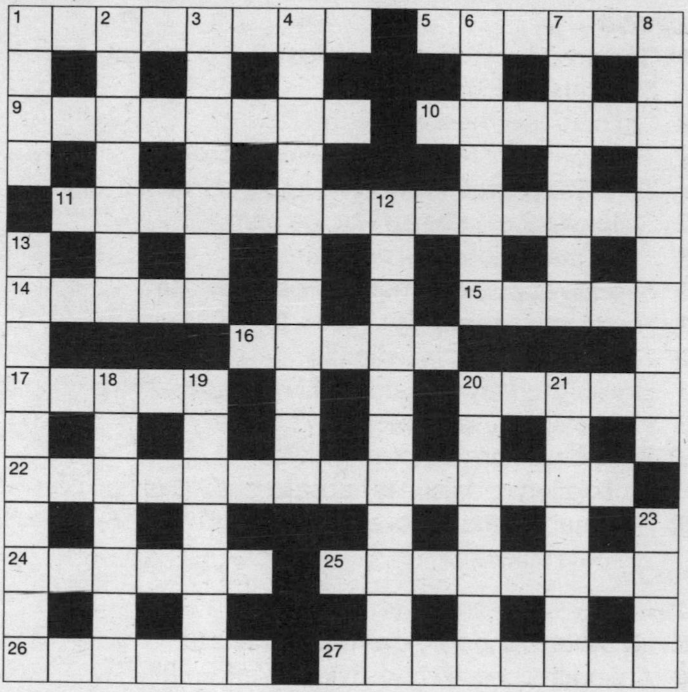

Across

1 Devote yourself to the goddess in 1 down rather than the god (4,4,3,3)
8 Girl carrier in the artillery (5)
9 Tiny lies indicate second childhood (8)
11 Something wrong with one at round Russian lake (7)
12 Sailor without father in France carries a light (7)
13 I give but Latin when medicated (5)
15 A rogue about testamentary business (9)
17 I need muse to expose Furies (9)
20 Code — this also is Latin (5)
21 Infelicitous way to make the National Health pay up (7)
23 9 begins in Russian sea with a military storehouse (7)
25 Secret session for home movies? (2,6)
26 Among forwards one is liable to peel till exhausted (5)
27 Raphael's "Whales love plump birds"? (6,2,6)

Down

1 Botticelli's "Planets" (4,3,5)
2 Hill where King met Cromwell? (5)
3 Abandons beastly home near Watford (9)
4 Caller puts it into an eye-shield (7)
5 Outside poles, not work that's continuous (3-4)
6 Flower, thou art translated by the border! (5)
7 Sequel to a French expression at Hindhead (9)
10 First day at 27? Never! (5,7)
14 Harmonious year at the speed of sound, about (9)
16 Clear round — go away! — or go too far (9)
18 Battery for a teetotaller in prison? (3,4)
19 Seal for an accountant in person? (3,4)
22 A plot for 27? (5)
24 Effect of sound on one in the front of an aircraft (5)

94

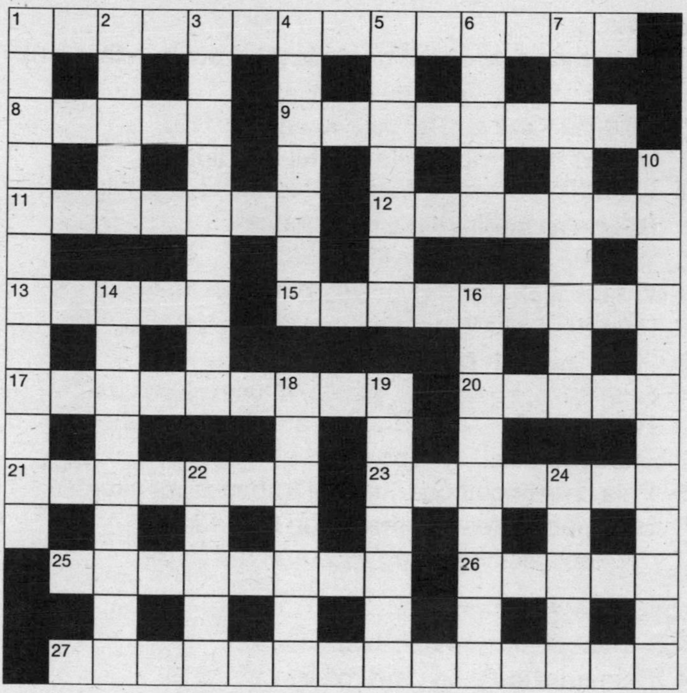

Across

1 French ridicule about endless 20 down in Africa (10)
8 Famous player, maybe in 26 (4)
10 Pole, so I found in 26, is a keen type (10)
11 Middle 26's brains outside the academy (4)
13 See 12
15 Design as applied to a rug? (6)
16 Worship according to Paul? (6)
17 What envelopes are for? (8,7)
18 Pole swallows it, not wishing to give offence? (6)
20 Half-size, with plenty of 10 (6)
21 South African beggar, perhaps, who ruled Portugal (7)
22 The days of a little king? (4)
25 Pole cheating about student's literary activity (10)
26 Direction for festival that hasn't started (4)
27 It's Rabelaisian to long for a thin dish (10)

Down

2,3 Past performances? (8)
4 Second should be paid for (6)
5 An 11 nag unique? Hardly — it's one of fifty (15)
6 Comparatively 26 festival? (6)
7 Request cot with hoops etc (7,3)
9 The mutinous fifty's little changed after ninety minutes (5,5)
12,13 across Request two pounds cash ever? They'd come in useful (10,7)
13 Ginger's vehicle is decaying (7)
14 Colonial peacemaker? (7)
15 Stuff for puff (4,6)
19 26 curve on a piano as protection to the listener (3-3)
20 Ambitious start between extremes in Africa (6)
23 Storyteller on the way back? (4)
24 Fever will be universal in time (4)

95

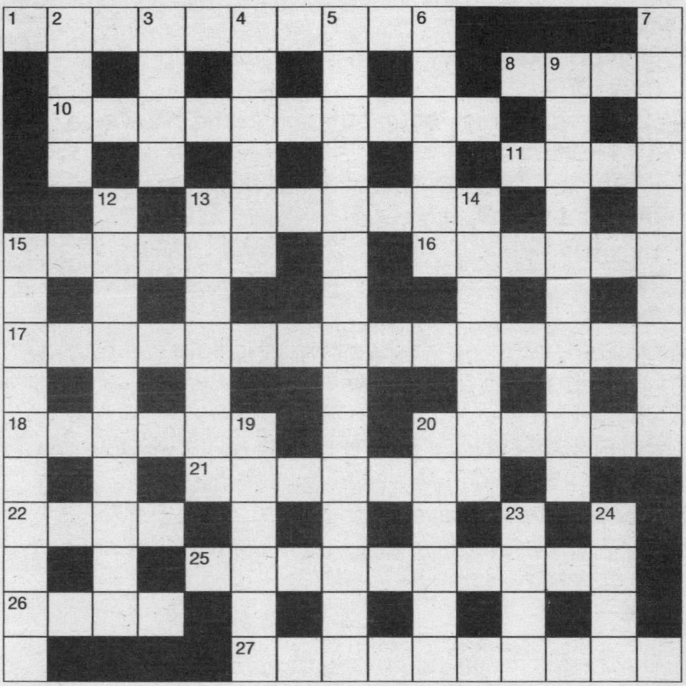

Across

9 One pound, if returned, in strange surroundings will melt (9)

10,12 Revolutionary coup fitting in a little bit above 4 14 across (5,7)

11 Worthless creature, or lamented friend, dodged a different way (4,3)

12 See 10

13 Three Rs, one as heard, on a lower frequency (5)

14 See 4

16 Old-time evening classes involving light reading? (7,8)

19 Direction to go to sea thus (9)

21 +h (5)

22,23 First-class service without 19 has a warlike sound above 25 (3,4-7)

24 The beast's sent everything back to mother (5)

25 Othello's about a denarius income: with the start of 22 across he's above 10 12 (9)

Down

1 Dull series for calculators (5,5)

2,3 One quarrel adds variety to a major equivalent (8,6)

4,14 across Achieve honours: chap with red back above 2 3 (4,9)

5 Bump! Cornet goes flat on his face (10)

6 Stimulate the works with an aubergine (8)

7 To defend oneself in an unspecified direction (6)

8 Length of 4s (4)

14 About once round the valleys to gain strength? (10)

15 Old-time candlestick to hurry last year's winner (4-6)

17 Racial trouble in chalet (8)

18 Approximate weight of a village near Cromer (8)

20 Noise of a waking lion? (6)

21,22 Good-looking individual, and clever? (10)

23 In myself, I am acting without speaking (4)

96

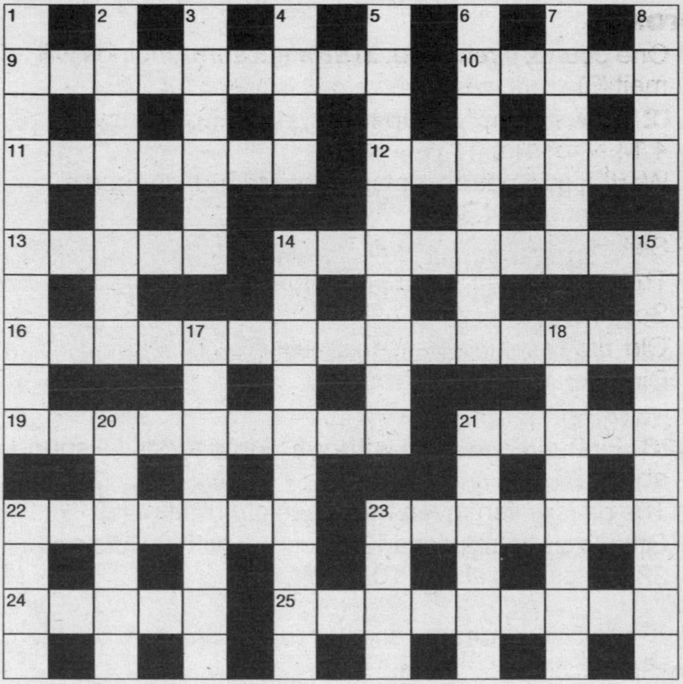

Across

9 Drugged animal on its dignity (4,5)
10 Nothing that exists, they say, is green (5)
11 Wagnerian art isn't needed (7)
12 Small letter (not E) permitted (7)
13 End of the game: get married! (4)
14 See 17
16 Film prize about half full, for kissing? (7)
17,14 Fireweed got up with laurel will bend her bow (7,10)
19,20 Angelology merged with Anglesey representative (5,5,6)
22 Mark left by southern vehicle (4)
24 One pound one shilling's for a king's 13 (7)
25 Metal threads follow footsteps — over stile? (4,3)
26 Music from Corfu guesthouse (5)
27 River rose to fill it? (9)

Down

1 From birth to death I greatly enjoyed myself (3,4,2,2,4)
2 Selfish cities go to ruin (8)
3 European associated with 15 less North Dakota (5)
4 See 6
5 Kenneth backing Leonard for 25? (6)
6,4 Imperial war site presents thornier problem round one end of cathedral, maybe (5-4,8)
7 11's 13 that's about disposed of (6)
8 The question of sex in the very young (2,2,1,3,2,1,4)
15 Shed blood below the heart as someone did at Balaclava (9)
17 Cavalier may be one to slay Roundhead (8)
18 Rood (4,4)
20 See 19
21 Craving concerning glory (6)
23 The pain of being fashionable? (5)

97

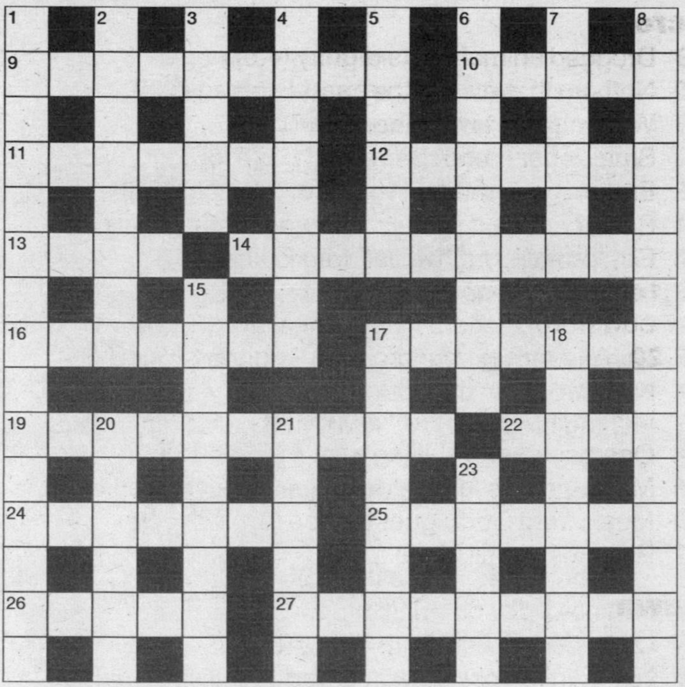

Across

1 None, then not none, like Brown's garden (8)
5 Composer, with luck, around Royal Oak (6)
9 Playwright to arrest American partner (8)
10 Professional models do, for health (6)
11 Rise mute, perhaps, when leaving chair? (8)
12 Part of England is malicious and gloomy (6)
14 Get the shine off the ball with Eric in (10)
18 How long a leap takes? (10)
22 Chancellor's concern with what little flower will fetch? (6)
23 Lain out around the bracken — underground? (8)
24 Fast one left in the soup? (6)
25 Painted black and white without curt exchange (8)
26 Call Dad back: it's Tarzan! (3,3)
27 Isles for man with more than one wife? (8)

Down

1 Girl who sounds like a boy (6)
2 Girl, flower, or colour (6)
3 Girl with concession to come (6)
4 Girl, a very small object, entertains disputant (10)
6 Girl has the creeper in a state (8)
7 Girl round about a boy (8)
8 Girl breaks the ankle (8)
13 Girl contributing to encirclement in Europe (10)
15 Girl is first to fall victim to Los Angeles (8)
16 Girl with the wisdom to be less than uncivil without money (8)
17 Girl with a heavenly article of flavouring (8)
19 Girl there's another form of! (6)
20 Girl inverts parts of Yorkshire (6)
21 Girl grown up in Grammar School? (6)

98

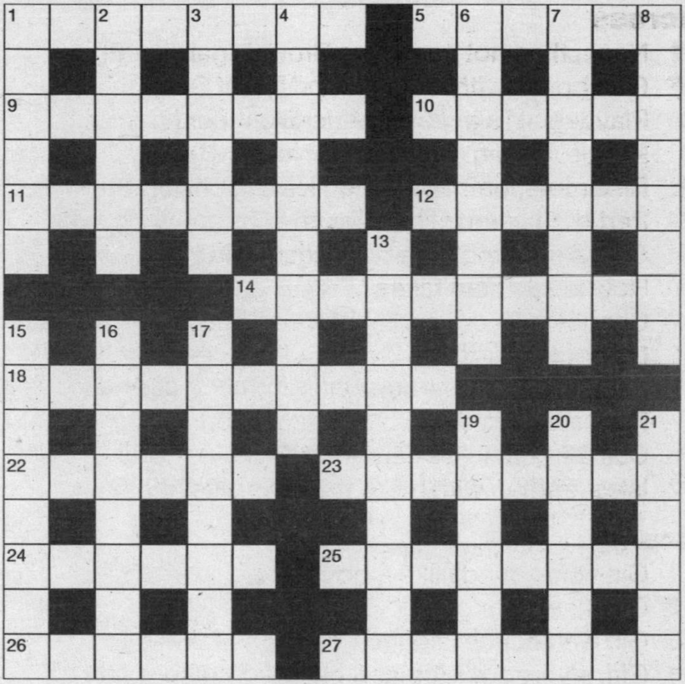

Across

1 Scot coming to start ringers on their object (8)
5 Out, like Fry's prisoners (6)
9 Roundabout kiln for cooking (8)
10 Flexible mountaineer losing his head (6)
12 Hat for the poll? (5)
13 Guild then seen in the dark (9)
14 Man an educational establishment? (5,7)
18 Big grouse about Liza in French company after frolic (12)
21 Train a Stuart? (5,4)
23 Make a woman of barbarian's former 'usband (or vice versa? (5)
24 Sprinkle sugar and remake bed? (6)
25 Going away, having reigned a century? (8)
26 Lets us off the struggle (6)
27 Ninevite, like Damascene? (8)

Down

1 The Church gets more money, being red! (6)
2 Not much — just about a string (6)
3 Night flier, result of the war, shouldn't be let out with baby (4,5)
4 The French language (Latin?) (6,6)
6 Psephological change at the fair (5)
7 Send me up some beer to poison relationships? (8)
8 Did imitations — standard thing, love having perished (8)
11 Prevent mail reaching capitals? (5,7)
15 The French one certainly is in no hurry (9)
16 Certify how to put money in the bank? (8)
17 New York's press displays agility (8)
19 St Francis's confession of folly? (6)
20 O (6)
22 A joint on a plate is allowed (5)

99

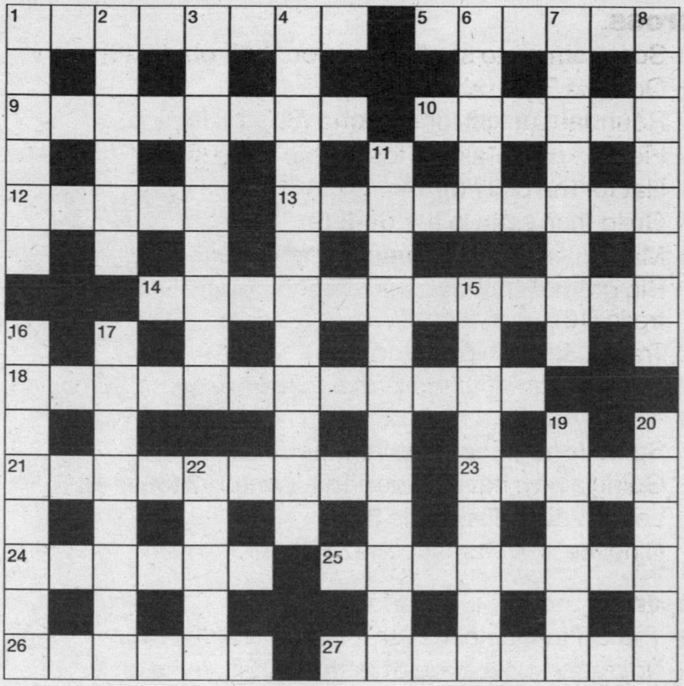

Across

8 Acknowledgement for turning out without a wiper (5,3)
9 Oriental rubbish, first century, about love (6)
10 Gardener's boy? (4)
11 Peripatetic bull with no tail in 9 (10)
12 Wine in the churchyard? (6)
14,15 English poet's rendering of Greek playwright ... (8,7)
17 ...by Latin playwright ... (7)
20 ... and English playwright (8)
22 Staple requirements in the garden (6)
23 Clearly Cindy's tilt is different (10)
24 Abandoned Socialists? (4)
25 Well-known extract from the tale of a mouse (6)
26 Pulse of two fowls? (5-3)

Down

1 Stir or seethe, like the last! (8)
2 Rebuff to the nose? (4)
3 The way to avoid quiet in the awful abyss (6)
4 Dance with a bachelor — it's sweet! (3,4)
5 He will sink his putt in the Pit (8)
6 Dependant on a quota of soldiers (10)
7 Fruit — corn it could be (6)
13 Troublesome call is invitation (10)
16 A person of note up aloft? (8)
18 The last thing you'd expect from a hothead! (4,4)
19 Loose like a loser one has backed? (7)
21 Man first, perhaps, and other things? (6)
22 Old heathen to give money with minute return (6)
24 Enjoy, as it were? (4)

100

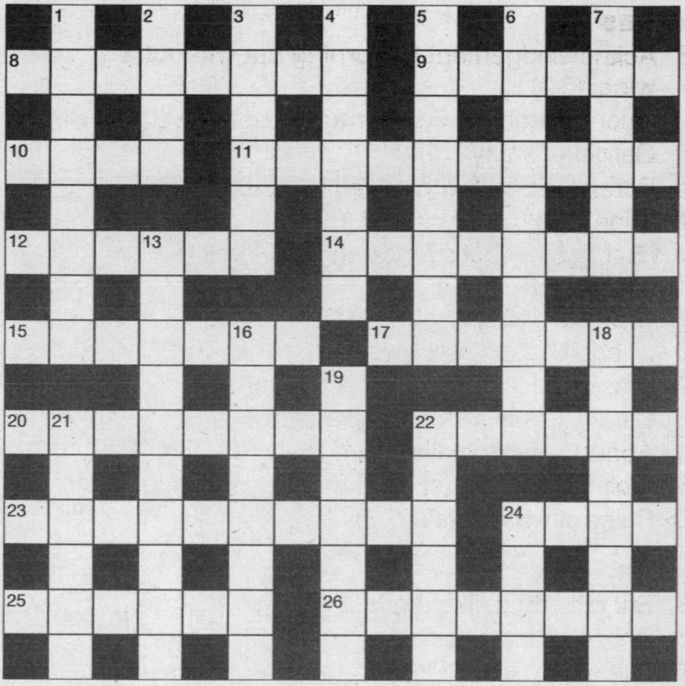

Solutions

1

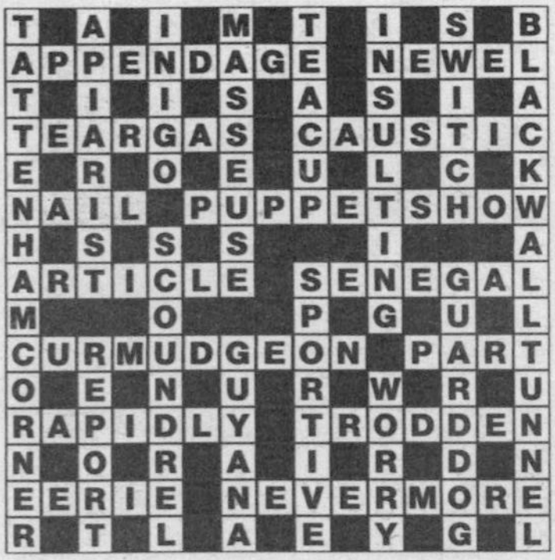
T A I M T I S B
APPENDAGE NEWEL
T I I S A S I A
TEARGAS CAUSTIC
E R O E U L C K
NAIL PUPPETSHOW
H S S S I A
ARTICLE SENEGAL
M O P G U L
CURMUDGEON PART
O E N U R W R U
RAPIDLY TRODDEN
N O R A I R D N
EERIE NEVERMORE
R T L A E Y G L

2

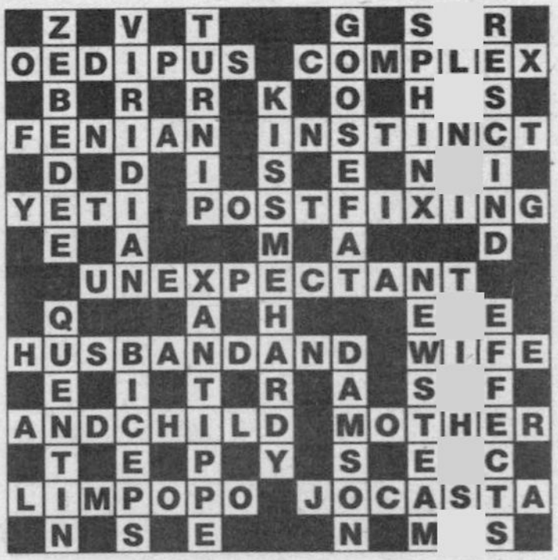
Z V T G S R
OEDIPUS COMPLEX
B R R K O H S
FENIAN INSTINCT
D D I S E N I
YETI POSTFIXING
E A M A D
UNEXPECTANT
Q A H E E
HUSBANDAND WIFE
E I T R A S F
ANDCHILD MOTHER
T E P Y S E C
LIMPOPO JOCASTA
N S E N M S

FATIGUE POSTMAN
A A R R R N A A
LIKEARATINATRAP
L E V S N I K H
OUNCE EXCELLENT
U F L I T H
TROOPSHIP DOGMA
R I U L I A
BIGOT MAELSTROM
A R A P D A
REARRANGE AVERT
R N I K X R N I
INTENSIFICATION
E E G N L T N E
REDFORD EPERGNE

3

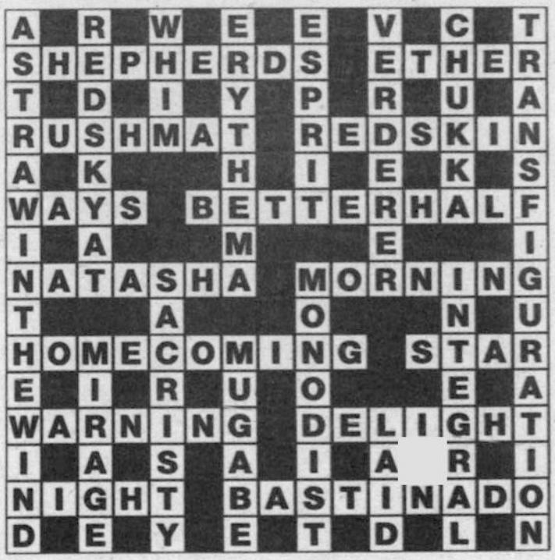
A R W E E V C T
SHEPHERDS ETHER
T D I Y P R U A
RUSHMAT REDSKIN
A K H I E K S
WAYS BETTERHALF
I A M E I
NATASHA MORNING
T A O N U
HOMECOMING STAR
E I R U O E A
WARNING DELIGHT
I A S A I A R I
NIGHT BASTINADO
D E Y E T D L N

4

5 **6**

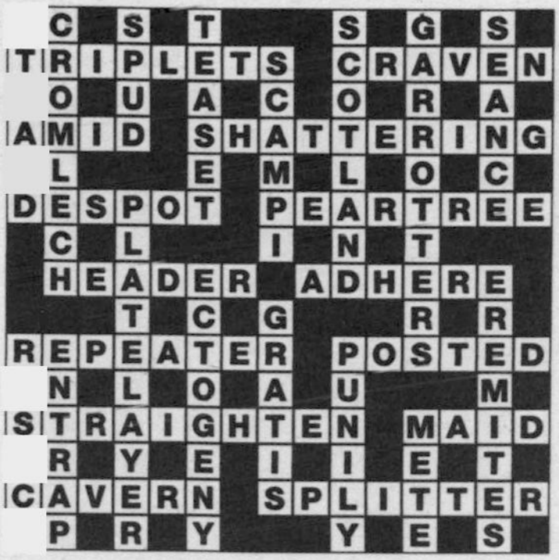
C S T S G S
TRIPLETS CRAVEN
O U A C O R A
AMID SHATTERING
L E M L O C
DESPOT PEARTREE
C L I N T
HEADER ADHERE
T C G R R
REPEATER POSTED
N L O A U M
STRAIGHTEN MAID
R Y E I I E T
CAVERN SPLITTER
P R Y Y E S

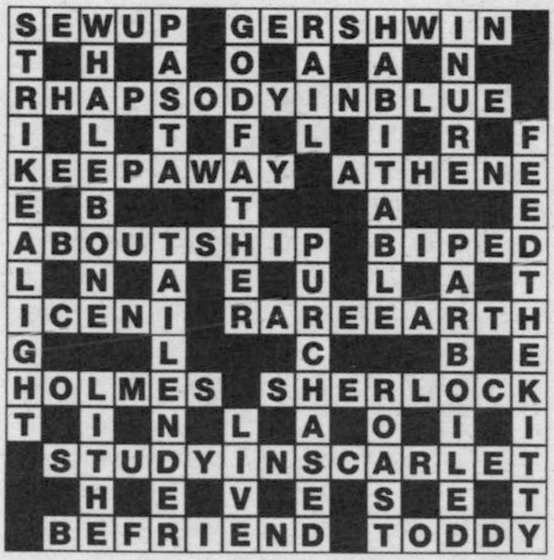
SEWUP GERSHWIN
T H A O A A N
RHAPSODYINBLUE
I L T F L I R F
KEEPAWAY ATHENE
E B T A E
ABOUTSHIP BIPED
L N A E U L A T
ICENI RAREEARTH
G L C B E
HOLMES SHERLOCK
T I N L A O I I
STUDYINSCARLET
H E V E S E T
BEFRIEND TODDY

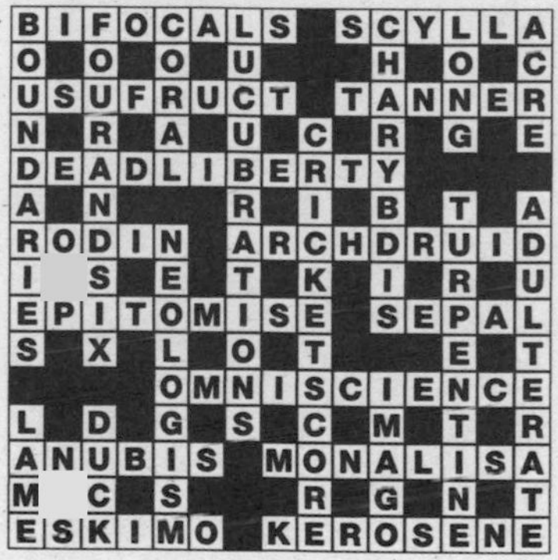
BIFOCALS SCYLLA
O O O O U H O C
USUFRUCT TANNER
N R A U C R G E
DEADLIBERTY
A N R I B T A
RODIN ARCHDRUID
I S E T K I R U
EPITOMISE SEPAL
S X L O T E T
OMNISCIENCE
L D G S C M T R
ANUBIS MONALISA
M C S R G N T
ESKIMO KEROSENE

FULLSUPPORT
C A I W R F H B
AMMONIA ORVIETO
R I E H T E T N
VALENTINE ROWAN
E Y L U O O E
ROCK FIRSTNIGHT
O N A E
WENTONFOOT INCH
I C T O T T A
VOLTI RETICULUM
E A O G I A E L
REVENGE LARAMIE
N E A R I D E T
SILLYSEASON

7 **8**

9

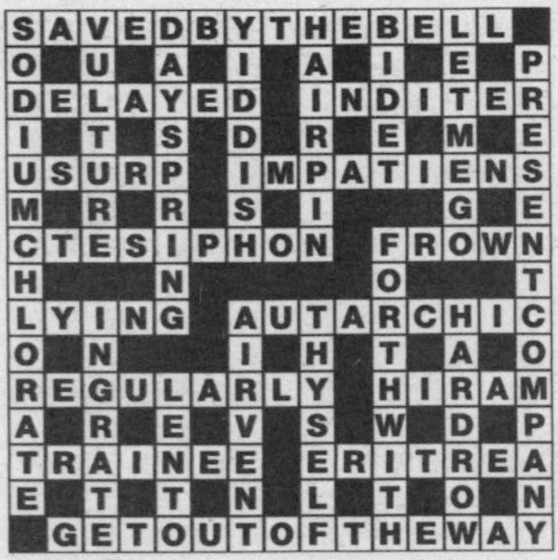
SAVEDBYTHEBELL
DELAYED INDITER
USURP IMPATIENS
CTESIPHON FROWN
LYING AUTARCHIC
REGULARLY HIRAM
TRAINEE ERITREA
GETOUTOFTHEWAY

10

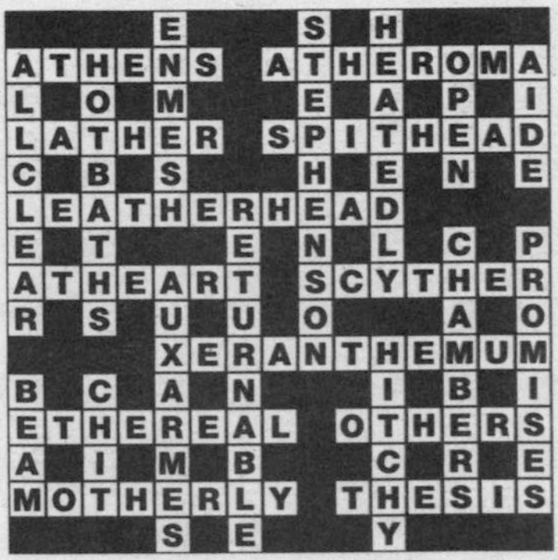
ATHENS ATHEROMA
LATHER SPITHEAD
LEATHERHEAD
ATHEART SCYTHER
XERANTHEMUM
ETHEREAL OTHERS
MOTHERLY THESIS

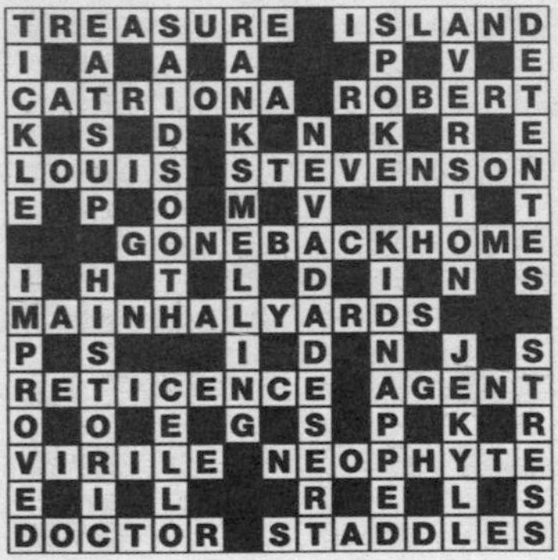
TREASURE ISLAND
CATRIONA ROBERT
LOUIS STEVENSON
GONEBACKHOME
MAINHALYARDS
RETICENCE AGENT
VIRILE NEOPHYTE
DOCTOR STADDLES

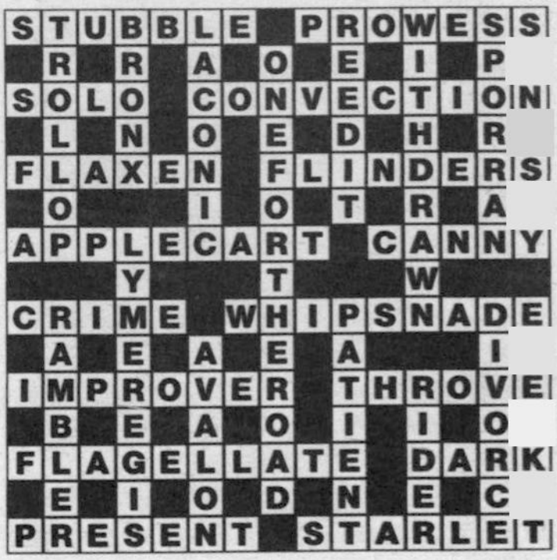
STUBBLE PROWESS
SOLO CONVECTION
FLAXEN FLINDERS
APPLECART CANNY
CRIME WHIPSNADE
IMPROVER THROVE
FLAGELLATE DARK
PRESENT STARLET

11

12

13

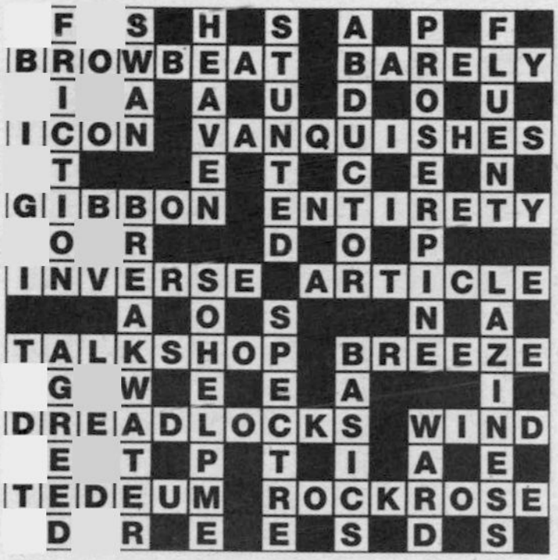

14

15

16

17

H	A	R	O	L	D		A	B	R	A	H	A	M	S
I		E		O				O		L		R		A
G	E	C	K	O		B	A	B	Y	B	U	G	G	Y
H		O		S		O		S		A		O		I
C	A	R	P	E	N	T	R	Y		N	I	S	A	N
O		D				T		O		B		Y		G
S	P	E	A	K	V	O	L	U	M	E	S			
T		R		O		M		R		R		A		A
			P	A	R	L	O	U	R	G	A	M	E	S
R		D		L		E		N				B		O
H	Y	E	N	A		S	E	C	E	S	S	I	O	N
Y		E		B		S		L		E		T		E
T	O	P	P	E	O	P	L	E		P	R	I	S	M
H		E		A		I				I		O		A
M	I	N	O	R	I	T	Y		C	A	N	N	O	N

18

S	I	N	G	L	E	C	U	R	R	E	N	C	Y	
A		A		A		H		E		D		U		O
N	E	V	E	R	L	A	N	D		W	O	R	D	S
D		A		G		R		U		I		R		T
W	O	R	T	H		R	A	C	O	N	T	E	U	R
I		I		E		I		E				N		I
C	O	N	S	T	A	N	T		E	M	E	T	I	C
H				T		G		S		I				H
B	A	M	B	O	O		S	T	A	N	D	O	F	F
O		U				A		E		U		U		E
A	I	R	B	U	B	B	L	E		S	U	T	R	A
R		D		N		B		R		F		F		T
D	R	O	O	D		A	Y	A	T	O	L	L	A	H
S		C		E		C		G		U		O		E
	T	H	I	R	T	Y	Y	E	A	R	S	W	A	R

	W	H	A	T	H	O		H	E	R	O	I	C	
	A		L		A		M		Y		F		O	
A	G	R	A		C	O	A	L	E	F	F	E	C	T
	O		R		K		D		L		T		O	
A	N	I	M	U	S		E	P	I	P	H	A	N	Y
	E				A		T		D		E		U	
B	R	U	S	H	W	O	O	D		S	P	I	T	
			H				M				E			
	P	L	O	T		V	E	S	T	I	G	I	A	L
	U		R		S		A		I				L	
S	T	I	T	C	H	E	S		G	O	B	B	L	E
	U		L		U		U		H		A		O	
S	P	O	I	L	T	B	R	A	T		G	I	V	E
	O		S		U		E		E		E		E	
	R	E	T	Y	P	E		A	N	G	L	E	R	

19

M	U	S	I	C	H	A	L	L			A	S	I	A
A		U		I		R		A		A		I		S
H	O	M	E	R		C	O	M	P	L	E	X	U	S
A		A		C		H		B		F		T		I
R	E	C	L	U	S	E		A	I	R	L	E	S	S
A				M		R		L		E		E		T
J	O	U	R	N	E	Y	S	E	N	D	I	N		
A		N		A						D		P		I
		L	O	V	E	R	S	M	E	E	T	I	N	G
O		E		I		E		O		M				N
F	R	A	U	G	H	T		I	N	U	T	E	R	O
F		R		A		O		S		S		W		R
C	O	N	S	T	R	U	C	T		S	P	I	C	A
U		E		E		C		E		E		N		N
T	I	D	E			H	A	R	D	T	O	G	E	T

20

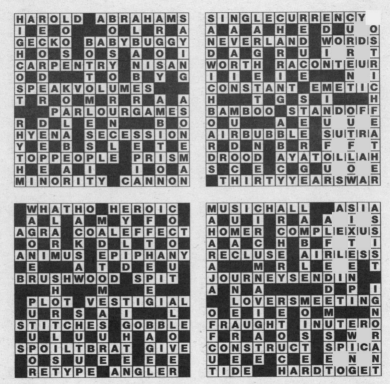

21

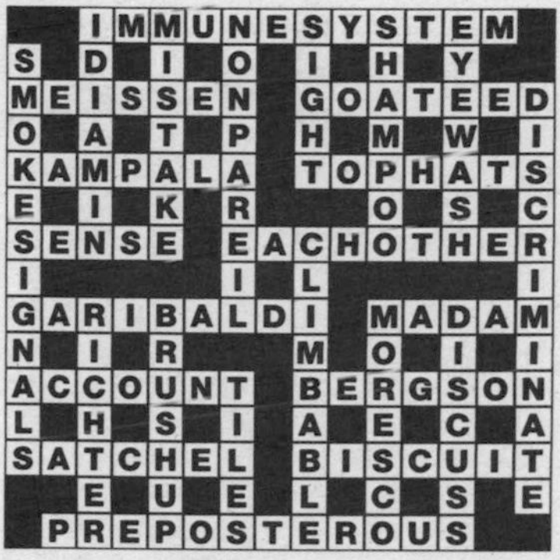
IMMUNESYSTEM
MEISSEN
GOATEED
KAMPALA
TOPHATS
SENSE
EACHOTHER
GARIBALDI
MADAM
ACCOUNT
BERGSON
SATCHEL
BISCUIT
PREPOSTEROUS

22

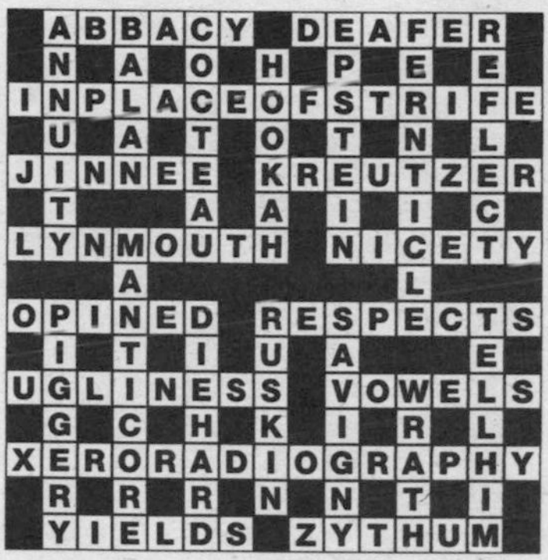
ABBACY
DEAFER
INPLACEOFSTRIFE
JINNEE
KREUTZER
LYNMOUTH
NICETY
OPINED
RESPECTS
UGLINESS
VOWELS
XERORADIOGRAPHY
YIELDS
ZYTHUM

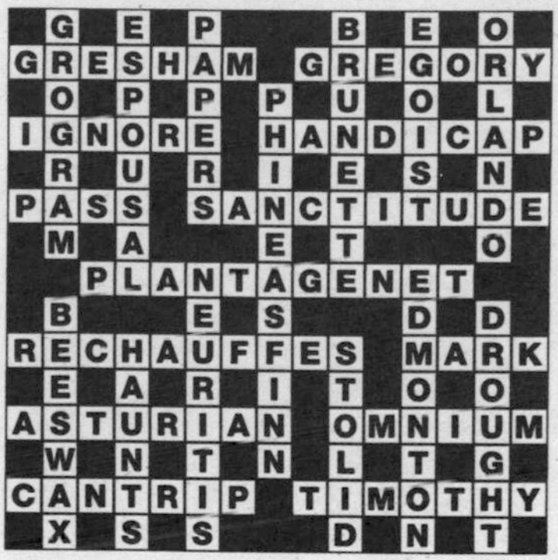
GRESHAM
GREGORY
IGNORE
HANDICAP
PASS
SANCTITUDE
PLANTAGENET
RECHAUFFES
MARK
ASTURIAN
OMNIUM
CANTRIP
TIMOTHY

23

KICKTHEBUCKET
AMPERSAND
ARGON
LEEDS
SPAGHETTI
WESTERN
PONTIFF
LADYBUG
LASTWAR
SOAPOPERA
SIREN
ELAND
TENORBELL
CHOREOGRAPHER

24

25

W	I	T	H	M	E			G	R	O	W	O	L	D
I		A		O		L		W		F		D		I
D	I	S	E	M	B	O	D	Y		A	L	O	N	G
E		S		E		A		N		G		N		E
B	R	O	W	N		T	H	E	B	E	S	T	I	S
O				T		H		D				A		T
Y	E	T	T	O	B	E		D	E	F	I	L	E	
		O		U						O		G		
	A	M	U	S	E	D		F	O	R	S	Y	T	E
S		S				R		A		M				V
C	O	C	K	S	C	O	M	B		U	N	C	L	E
A		A		P		S		R		L		R		S
R	A	B	B	I		E	L	I	Z	A	B	E	T	H
A		I		T		R		C		T		E		A
B	E	N	E	Z	R	A			B	E	L	D	A	M

26

B	U	M	B	L	E		Q	U	I	X	O	T	I	C
E		O		A				N		A		I		E
E	N	I	G	M	A		H	O	O	V	E	R	E	D
S		D		I				P		I		A		A
	Y	O	U	N	G	P	R	E	T	E	N	D	E	R
		R		A		E		R		R		E		T
G	R	E	A	T	G	R	E	A	T		I	S	A	R
R				E		S		T		F				E
A	U	K	S		R	E	S	I	L	I	E	N	C	E
N		H		V		V		V		F		A		
D	I	E	S	E	L	E	L	E	C	T	R	I	C	
S		D		N		R				I		V		Z
O	L	I	V	E	O	I	L		J	E	R	E	M	Y
N		V		E		N				T		T		M
S	T	E	E	R	A	G	E		W	H	E	E	Z	E

27

C	A	T	W	A	L	K		C	O	W	S	L	I	P
O		E		L		A		A		O		Y		L
R	A	M	A	L		T	I	G	E	R	H	I	D	E
O		P		A		H		O		L		N		N
L	I	O	N	H	E	A	R	T		D	O	G	M	A
L		R				R				L				R
A	N	I	G	H		T	U	R	N	I	P	F	L	Y
		S		O		I		E		N		R		
D	E	E	R	L	I	C	K	S		G	R	I	M	M
E				L				I				T		O
F	I	S	H	Y		B	U	L	L	D	O	Z	E	R
I		P		H		R		I		I		L		I
C	R	O	C	O	D	I	L	E		T	E	A	R	S
I		O		C		N		N		T		N		O
T	U	R	N	K	E	Y		T	H	O	U	G	H	T

28

T		P		N		I		Y		I		S		T
H	A	L	F	O	U	N	C	E		D	U	T	C	H
I		A		R		T		L		E		R		E
N	E	C	K	T	I	E		L	E	A	D	O	F	F
S		E		H		R		O		L		U		I
L	A	N	D		V	I	E	W	F	I	N	D	E	R
I		T		C		O				S				S
C	O	A	C	H	E	R		D	E	T	R	O	I	T
E				A				E		S		D		R
D	I	C	T	I	O	N	A	R	Y		F	O	R	E
B		H		R		A		E		U		N		A
R	A	R	E	B	I	T		L	I	M	I	T	E	D
E		O		E		H		I		B		O		I
A	R	M	E	D		A	C	C	R	E	T	I	O	N
D		E		S		N		T		R		D		G

29

PLAYSAFE EMBRYO
U R H R A E L
TERMITES STUPID
S A N E T U F
KNIGHTBACHELOR
P G L H R E S I
EVERY I C WHERE
N INTHE N
TRICK K D WORLD
O N I E I A E S
PASSPORTOFFICE
A I L C F L B
PASSIM WELLTODO
E T N S E S O
RESIGN NEWSPEAK

30

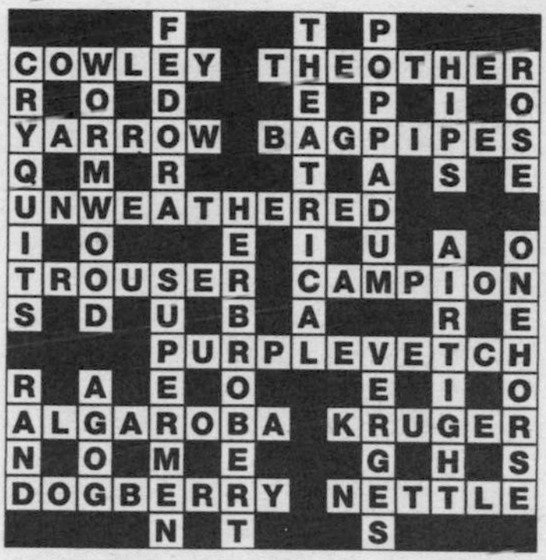
F T P
COWLEY THEOTHER
R O D E P I O
YARROW BAGPIPES
Q M R T A S E
UNWEATHERED
I O E I U A O
TROUSER CAMPION
S D U B A R E
PURPLEVETCH
R A E O E I O
ALGAROBA KRUGER
N O M E G H S
DOGBERRY NETTLE
N T S

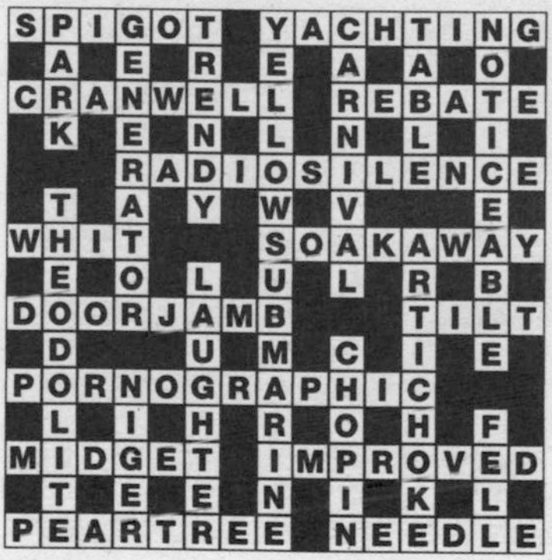
SPIGOT YACHTING
A E R E A A O
CRANWELL REBATE
K E N L N L I
RADIOSILENCE
T A Y W V E
WHIT SOAKAWAY
E O L U L R B
DOORJAMB TILT
D U M C I E
PORNOGRAPHIC
L I H R O H F
MIDGET IMPROVED
T E E N I K L
PEARTREE NEEDLE

31

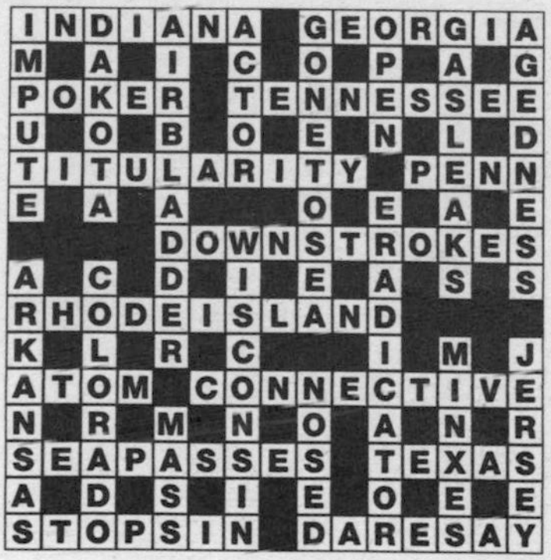
INDIANA GEORGIA
M A I C O P A G
POKER TENNESSEE
U O B O E N L D
TITULARITY PENN
E A A O E A E
DOWNSTROKES
A C D I E A S S
RHODEISLAND
K L R C I M J
ATOM CONNECTIVE
N R M N O A N R
SEAPASSES TEXAS
A D S I E O E E
STOPSIN DARESAY

32

33

M	A	K	E	W	A	R		A	B	Y	S	M	A	L
A		A		A		E		N		O		I		I
G	E	N	U	S		S	A	T	Y	R	I	C	O	N
P		S		H		E		I		K		H		E
I	T	A	L	I	C	T	Y	P	E		M	I	S	S
E		S		N				H		W		G		M
				G	U	L	F	O	F	A	Q	A	B	A
N		V		T		O		N		L		N		N
E	P	I	L	O	G	U	I	S	E	D				
B		R		N		I				E		N		S
R	A	G	E		A	S	T	R	I	N	G	E	N	T
A		I		I		I		H		S		V		R
S	Y	N	C	O	P	A	T	E		I	D	A	H	O
K		I		W		N		U		A		D		M
A	L	A	B	A	M	A		M	O	N	T	A	N	A

34

W	I	N	E	C	U	P		M	A	U	R	I	A	C
A		O		A		O		I		T		L		A
F	A	T	A	L		W	A	S	S	A	I	L	E	R
F		I		I		E		T		H		I		O
L	U	C	I	F	E	R	I	A	N		A	N	I	L
E		E		O				U		D		O		I
				R	E	M	I	G	R	A	T	I	O	N
C		M		N		I		H		Y		S		A
O	P	I	N	I	O	N	A	T	E	D				
L		S		A		N				R		M		C
U	R	S	A		T	E	M	P	L	E	B	E	L	L
M		O		O		S		S		A		X		I
B	R	U	S	H	W	O	R	K		M	A	I	N	E
I		R		I		T		O		E		C		N
A	R	I	Z	O	N	A		V	E	R	M	O	N	T

W	Y	O	M	I	N	G		H	A	M	M	O	N	D
R		R		D		I		A		A		K		E
O	B	E	S	E		H	O	M	E	R	U	L	E	R
N		G		A		O		P		Y		A		B
G	O	O	D	L	I	N	E	S	S		T	H	E	Y
S		N		I				H		C		O		D
				S	E	P	T	I	C	A	E	M	I	A
K		D		T		I		R		G		A		Y
E	V	E	N	I	N	G	B	E	L	L				
N		L		C		M				I		H		A
T	R	A	P		L	E	A	S	T	O	F	A	L	L
U		W		L		N		E		S		W		A
C	H	A	R	A	C	T	E	R		T	E	A	R	S
K		R		N		E		I		R		I		K
Y	I	E	L	D	E	D		F	L	O	R	I	D	A

35

	R		S		A		O		S		H		A	
W	H	O	M	E	V	E	R		Y	E	A	S	T	Y
	E		E		I		G		M		R		H	
L	O	N	E		S	W	A	M	P	A	D	D	E	R
	S				E		N		O		L		N	
S	T	Y	L	E	D		I	N	S	P	A	D	E	S
	A		A				C		I		B			
S	T	A	T	I	O	N		M	A	H	O	M	E	T
			I		P		H				U		M	
M	A	I	N	L	I	N	E		S	T	R	E	E	T
	L		C		U		A		P				R	
F	A	T	H	O	M	E	T	E	R		S	T	A	R
	B		A		D		H		U		E		L	
E	R	M	I	N	E		E	S	C	A	P	A	D	E
	I		R		N		N		E		T		S	

36

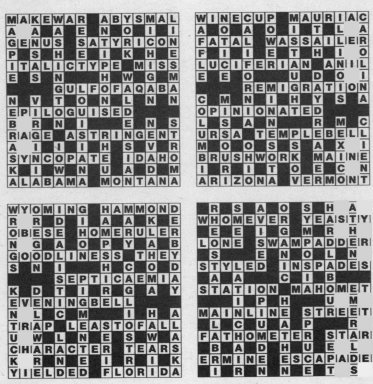

37

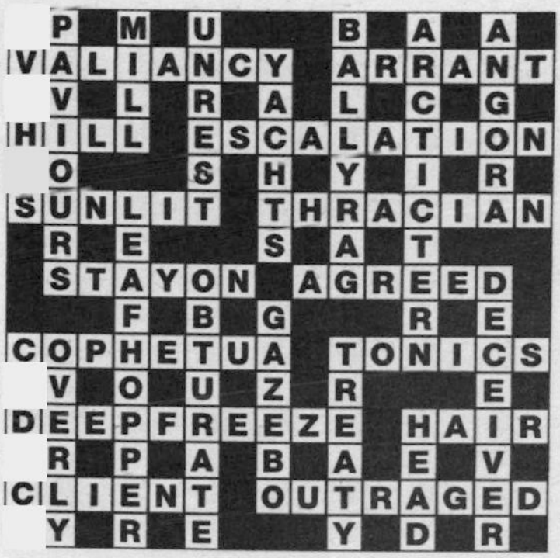
VALIANCY
ARRANT
HILL
ESCALATION
SUNLIT
THRACIAN
STAYON
AGREED
COPHETUA
TONICS
DEEPFREEZE
HAIR
CLIENT
OUTRAGED

38

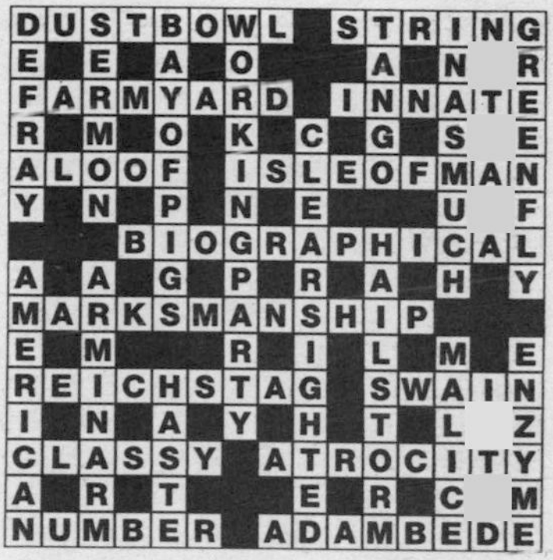
DUSTBOWL
STRING
FARMYARD
INNATE
ALOOF
ISLEOFMAN
BIOGRAPHICAL
MARKSMANSHIP
REICHSTAG
SWAIN
CLASSY
ATROCITY
NUMBER
ADAMBEDE

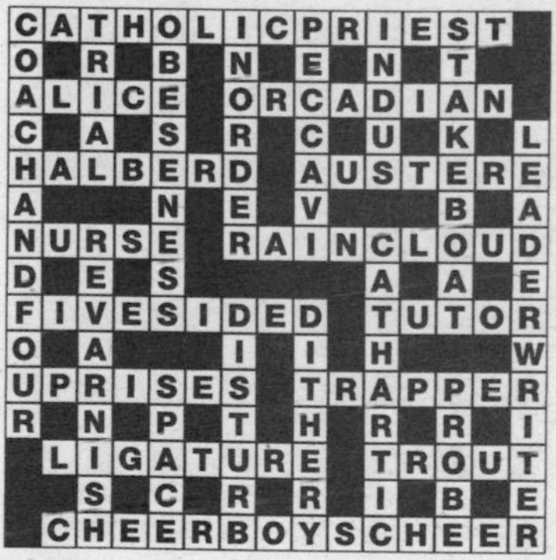
CATHOLICPRIEST
ALICE
ORCADIAN
HALBERD
AUSTERE
NURSE
RAINCLOUD
FIVESIDED
TUTOR
UPRISES
TRAPPER
LIGATURE
TROUT
CHEERBOYSCHEER

39

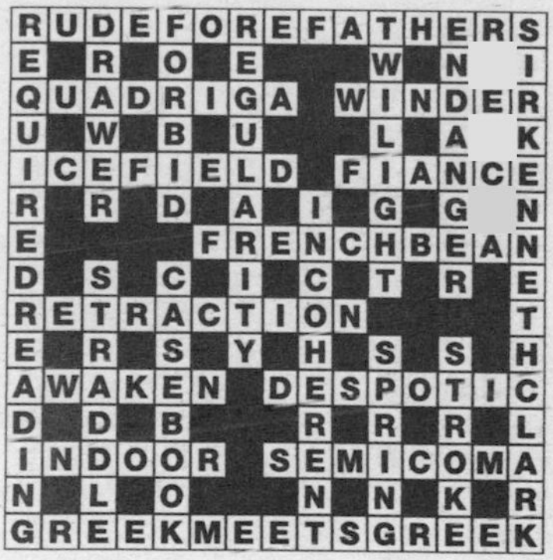
RUDEFOREFATHERS
QUADRIGA
WINDER
ICEFIELD
FIANCE
FRENCHBEAN
RETRACTION
AWAKEN
DESPOTIC
INDOOR
SEMICOMA
GREEKMEETSGREEK

40

41

HUDDERSFIELD
ORLEANS
RAMSTAM
BAFFLER
XEROTES
WAXED
VIZIERATE
TIPANDRUN
JOKES
YEAROFF
COCTION
USELESS
ARACHNE
QUEENSBEASTS

42

ALLEGRO
GASFIRE
SPIRIT
RETRENCH
RARA
CRANKSHAFT
LOOSESTRIFE
FREEFORALL
AVIS
MOTORCAR
BUFFER
HENGIST
FULSOME

LUGUBRIOUSNESS
XYLOPHONE
AMBER
CACTI
COSTARICA
GRANTHAM
ITSELF
ALWAYS
HOTMEALS
HEADLINES
TEMPI
RATED
RELIEFNIB
MACNAMARASBAND

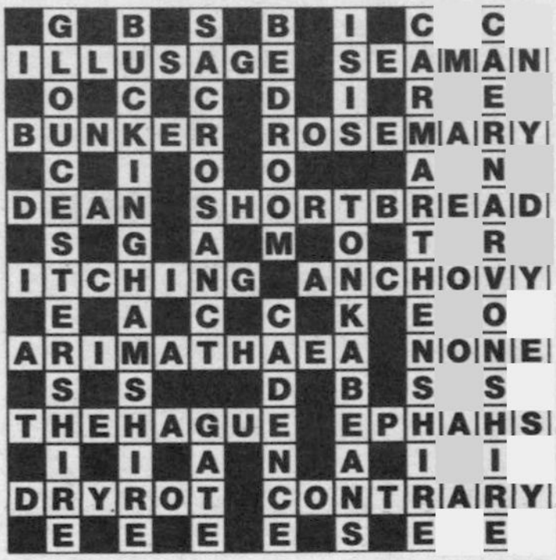

ILLUSAGE
SEAMAN
BUNKER
ROSEMARY
DEAN
SHORTBREAD
ITCHING
ANCHOVY
ARIMATHAEA
NONE
THEHAGUE
EPHAHS
DRYROT
CONTRARY

43

44

45

T	R	A	N	S	C	E	N	D	E	N	T	A	L	
H		C		A		X		A		E		P		P
E	N	H	A	N	C	E		H	O	G	A	R	T	H
R		A		G		C		O		U		I		I
M	O	T	I	F		U	N	M	U	S	I	C	A	L
O		E		R		T		E				O		A
D	I	S	C	O	V	E	R	Y		P	A	T	E	N
Y				I						L				T
N	O	T	E	D		B	A	C	H	A	R	A	C	H
A		E				E		H		Y		U		R
M	A	R	M	A	L	A	D	E		H	A	R	P	O
I		R		B		G		L		O		E		P
C	R	A	N	I	A	L		S	C	U	T	A	R	I
S		I		D		E		E		S		T		S
	U	N	D	E	R	S	T	A	T	E	M	E	N	T

46

	I	M	P	E	R	T	U	R	B	A	B	L	E	
J		I		A		H		I		R		Y		C
U	P	S	E	T	T	I	N	G		T	A	R	K	A
X		C		E		M		H		D		I		M
T	U	R	I	N		B	U	T	T	E	R	C	U	P
A		E				L		E		A				A
P	R	A	T	T	L	E		D	A	L	S	T	O	N
O		N		A						E		R		O
S	A	T	A	N	I	C		C	O	R	N	E	L	L
I				Q		H		A				B		O
T	R	U	C	U	L	E	N	T		D	Y	I	N	G
I		N		E		E		A		O		Z		I
O	T	T	E	R		R	E	L	I	G	I	O	U	S
N		I		A		U		A		G		N		T
	P	L	A	Y	U	P	O	N	W	O	R	D	S	

47

H	I	C	K	O	R	Y		D	I	C	K	O	R	Y
	S		U		U		U		N		I		O	
D	O	C	K		I	N	N	O	V	A	T	I	O	N
	L		R		N		A		E		T		K	
C	A	L	I	C	O		C	A	R	P	E	T	E	D
	T				U		C		T		N		R	
S	E	C	L	U	S	I	O	N		S	I	B	Y	L
			I				M				S			
L	E	A	V	E		A	P	A	R	T	H	E	I	D
	V		E		C		A		E				N	
P	E	A	R	M	A	I	N		F	A	M	I	S	H
	R		P		M		I		R		E		H	
A	T	M	O	S	P	H	E	R	E		N	O	O	K
	O		O		U		D		S		O		R	
E	N	G	L	I	S	H		C	H	A	N	N	E	L

48

H	A	C	K	S	A	W	S		A	D	D	L	E	D
E		O		I		A				E		I		I
R	A	P	A	C	I	T	Y		G	L	O	B	A	L
A		I		K		E				I		R		A
L	A	N	D	L	O	R	D		A	C	C	E	N	T
D		G		E		F		A		A		T		O
					P	R	O	S	E	C	U	T	O	R
O		S		B		O		T		Y		O		Y
V	E	T	E	R	I	N	A	R	Y					
E		A		O		T		O		S		W		C
R	E	N	O	W	N		F	L	E	T	C	H	E	R
D		D		N				O		A		I		E
R	E	P	O	S	E		A	G	I	T	A	T	E	D
A		A		E				E		I		E		I
W	I	T	H	A	L		P	R	E	C	I	N	C	T

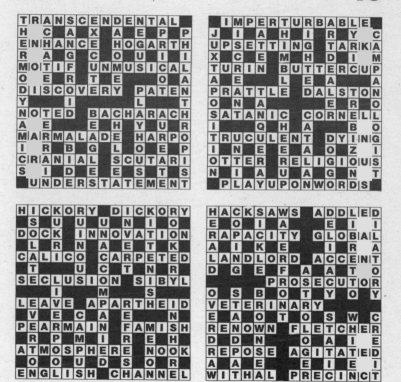

49

50

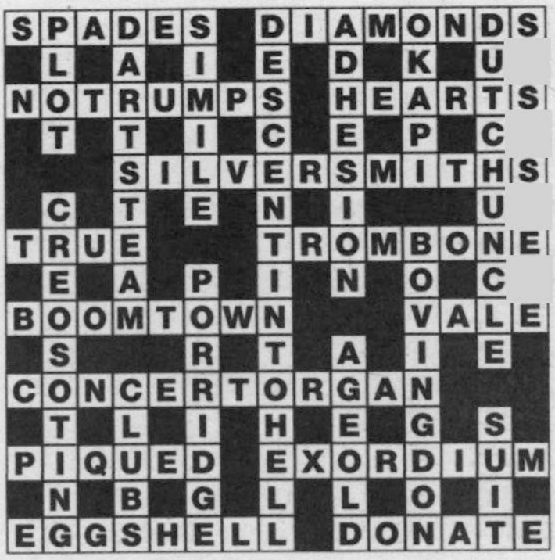

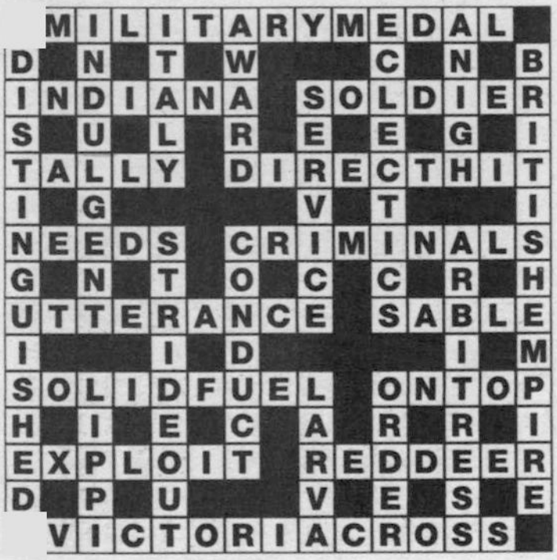

51

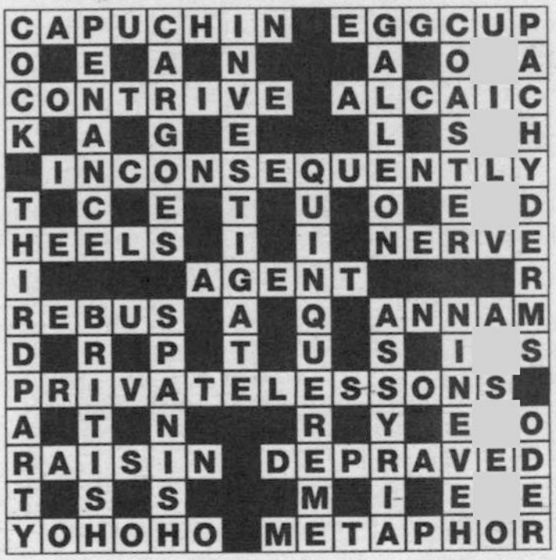

52

53

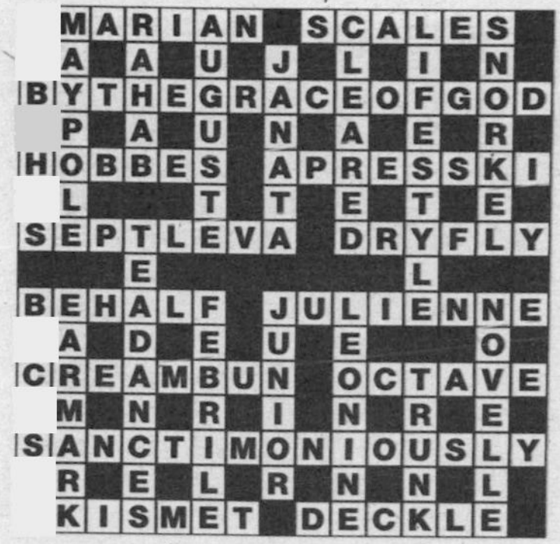
MARIAN SCALES
BYTHEGRACEOFGOD
HOBBES APRESSKI
SEPTLEVA DRYFLY
BEHALF JULIENNE
CREAMBUN OCTAVE
SANCTIMONIOUSLY
KISMET DECKLE

54

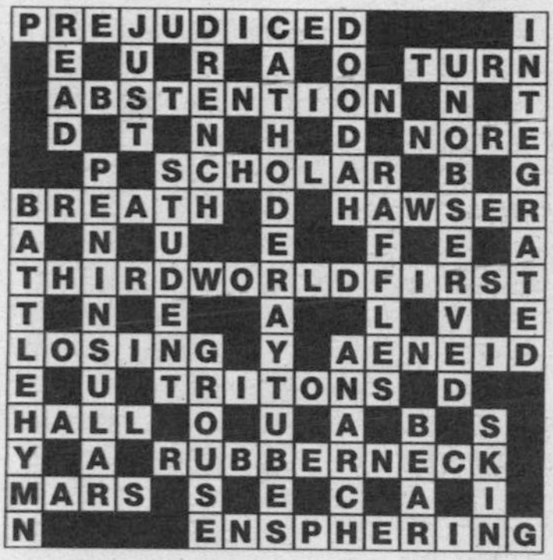
PREJUDICED
TURN
ABSTENTION
NORE
SCHOLAR
BREATH HAWSER
THIRDWORLDFIRST
LOSING AENEID
TRITONS
HALL
RUBBERNECK
MARS
ENSPHERING

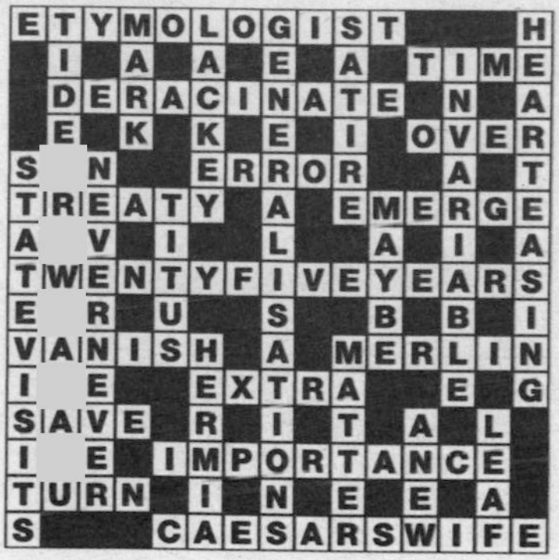
ETYMOLOGIST
TIME
DERACINATE
OVER
ERROR
TREATY EMERGE
TWENTYFIVEYEARS
VANISH MERLIN
EXTRA
SAVE
IMPORTANCE
TURN
CAESARSWIFE

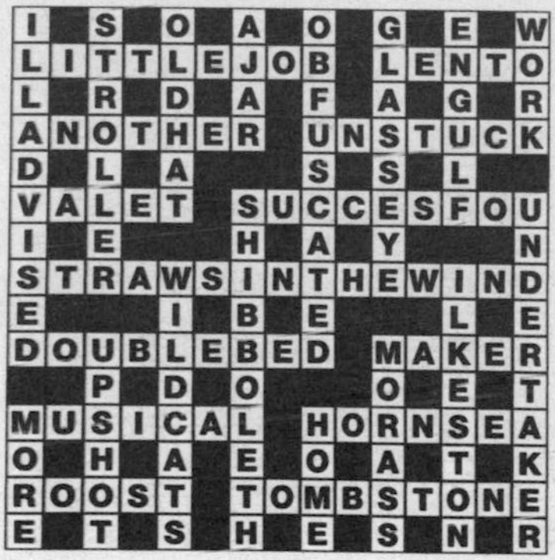
LITTLEJOB LENTO
ANOTHER UNSTUCK
VALET SUCCESFOU
STRAWSINTHEWIND
DOUBLEBED MAKER
MUSICAL HORNSEA
ROOST TOMBSTONE

55

56

57

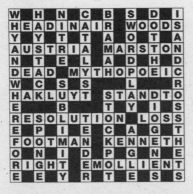

W	■	H	■	N	■	C	■	B	■	S	■	D	■	I
H	E	A	D	I	N	A	I	R	■	W	O	O	D	S
Y	■	Y	■	T	■	T	■	A	■	O	■	T	■	A
A	U	S	T	R	I	A	■	M	A	R	S	T	O	N
N	■	T	■	E	■	L	■	A	■	D	■	H	■	D
D	E	A	D	■	M	Y	T	H	O	P	O	E	I	C
W	■	C	■	S	■	S	■	■	■	L	■	■	■	R
H	A	K	L	U	Y	T	■	S	T	A	N	D	T	O
E	■	■	■	B	■	■	■	T	■	Y	■	I	■	S
R	E	S	O	L	U	T	I	O	N	■	L	O	S	S
E	■	P	■	I	■	E	■	C	■	A	■	G	■	T
F	O	O	T	M	A	N	■	K	E	N	N	E	T	H
O	■	N	■	I	■	D	■	P	■	G	■	N	■	E
R	I	G	H	T	■	E	M	O	L	L	I	E	N	T
E	■	E	■	Y	■	R	■	T	■	E	■	S	■	S

58

D	I	S	T	A	N	C	E	■	G	A	N	D	E	R
E	■	T	■	S	■	A	■	■	■	R	■	I		E
T	R	E	A	S	U	R	E	■	I	S	L	A	N	D
A	■	A	■	H	■	I	■	F	■	O	■	T		F
C	A	D	G	E	■	C	A	L	A	N	D	R	I	A
H	■	Y	■	G	■	A	■	A	■	■	■	I		C
■	■	■	C	O	N	T	E	M	P	T	I	B	L	E
D	■	C	■	E	■	U	■	E	■	R	■	E	■	D
I	L	L	U	S	T	R	A	T	I	O	N	■	■	■
S	■	A	■	■	■	I	■	H	■	U	■	T	■	S
P	U	R	C	H	A	S	E	R	■	B	E	E	C	H
O	■	I	■	O	■	T	■	O	■	L	■	D		O
S	A	N	I	T	Y	■	S	W	O	O	N	I	N	G
E	■	E	■	E	■	■	■	E	■	U	■	U		U
S	E	T	T	L	E	■	C	R	O	S	S	M	A	N

F	U	L	L	T	O	T	H	E	B	R	I	M	■	D
O	■	A	■	A	■	H	■	D	■	■	■	E	■	R
U	N	C	A	R	P	E	T	E	D	■	E	R	G	O
R	■	Q	■	N	■	P	■	N	■	M	■	C	■	W
T	R	U	J	I	L	L	O	■	S	A	T	U	R	N
E	■	E	■	S	■	A	■	R	■	R	■	R	■	O
E	A	R	T	H	■	N	■	O	■	S	A	Y	O	N
N	■	■	■	■	V	E	N	U	S	■	■	■	■	E
P	L	U	T	O	■	T	■	N	■	J	I	N	K	S
O	■	R	■	N	■	S	■	D	■	U	■	E	■	G
U	R	A	N	U	S	■	B	A	G	P	I	P	E	R
N	■	N	■	S	■	G	■	B	■	I	■	T	■	I
D	R	I	P	■	R	A	C	O	N	T	E	U	S	E
E	■	U	■	■	■	I	■	U	■	E	■	N	■	F
R	■	M	O	V	I	N	G	T	A	R	G	E	T	S

59

T	A	L	E	S	O	F	M	Y	S	T	E	R	Y	■
H	■	A	■	T	■	L	■	O	■	E	■	E	■	■
E	D	G	A	R	■	A	L	L	A	N	P	O	E	■
R	■	E	■	A	■	T	■	K	■	O	■	P		A
U	P	R	I	G	H	T	■	S	A	N	D	E	A	U
E	■	■	■	G	■	E	■	A	■	■	■	N		G
M	O	D	E	L	■	R	I	C	H	E	L	I	E	U
O	■	E	■	E	■	■	■	■	■	A	■	N		S
R	E	D	B	R	I	D	G	E	■	S	I	G	H	T
G	■	U	■	■	■	I	■	F	■	T	■	■	■	E
U	N	C	I	V	I	L	■	F	E	I	G	N	E	D
E	■	T	■	I	■	E	■	E	■	N	■	A		U
■	C	I	N	N	A	M	O	N	■	D	R	O	O	P
■	■	O	■	C	■	M	■	D	■	I	■	M		I
■	A	N	D	I	M	A	G	I	N	A	T	I	O	N

60

61

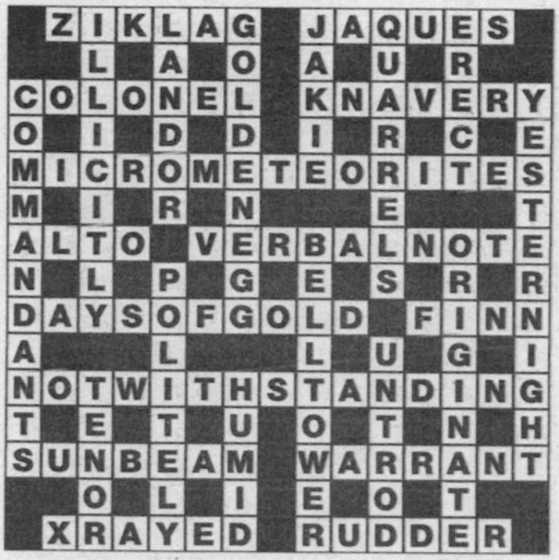
ZIKLAG JAQUES
L A O A U R
COLONEL KNAVERY
O I D D I R C E
MICROMETEORITES
M I R N E T
ALTO VERBALNOTE
N L P G E S R R
DAYSOFGOLD FINN
A L L U G I
NOTWITHSTANDING
T E T U O T N H
SUNBEAM WARRANT
O L I E O T
XRAYED RUDDER

62

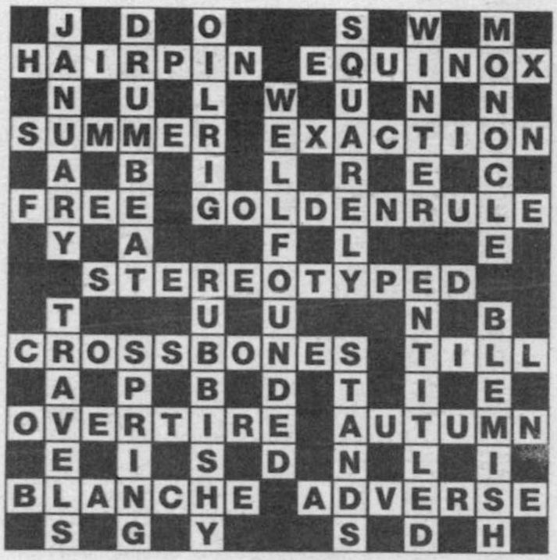
J D O S W M
HAIRPIN EQUINOX
N U L W U N N
SUMMER EXACTION
A B I L R E C
FREE GOLDENRULE
Y A F L E
STEREOTYPED
T U U N B
CROSSBONES TILL
A P B D T I E
OVERTIRE AUTUMN
E I S D N L I
BLANCHE ADVERSE
S G Y S D H

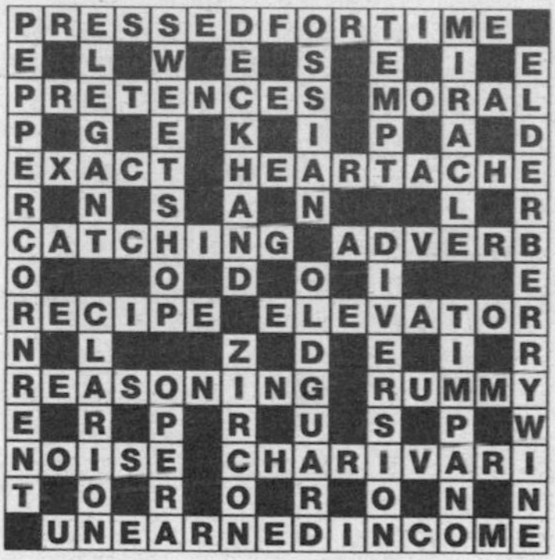
PRESSEDFORTIME
E L W E S E I E
PRETENCES MORAL
P G E K I P A D
EXACT HEARTACHE
R N S A N L R
CATCHING ADVERB
O O D O I E
RECIPE ELEVATOR
N L Z D E I R
REASONING RUMMY
E R P R U S P W
NOISE CHARIVARI
T O R O R O N N
UNEARNEDINCOME

63

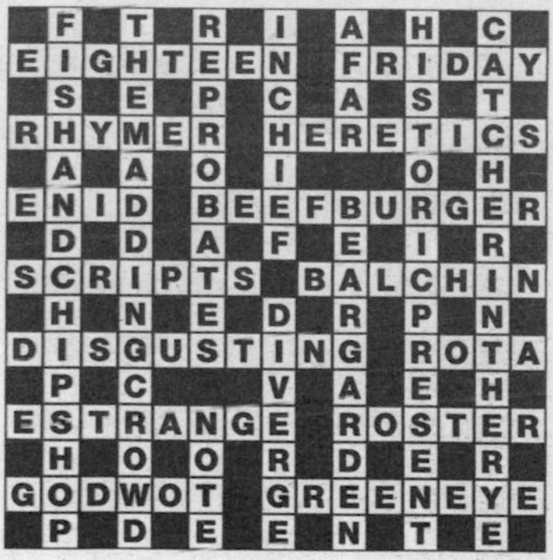
F T R I A H C
EIGHTEEN FRIDAY
S E P C A S T
RHYMER HERETICS
A A O I O H
ENID BEEFBURGER
D D A F E I R
SCRIPTS BALCHIN
H N E D R P N
DISGUSTING ROTA
P C V A E H
ESTRANGE ROSTER
H O O R D E R
GODWOT GREENEYE
P D E E N T E

64

65

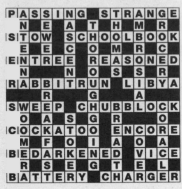

C	O	P	P	E	R	S	U	L	P	H	A	T	E	
A		R		A		A		I		O		A		P
S	P	O	R	R	A	N		B	L	U	B	B	E	R
T		D		L		D		R		S		L		E
L	O	U	S	Y		B	L	A	M	E	L	E	S	S
E		C		B		A		R				A		I
S	E	E	M	I	N	G	L	Y		D	R	U	I	D
I				R						O				E
N	O	M	A	D		W	H	E	E	L	S	P	I	N
S		A				H		N		A		L		T
P	H	Y	S	I	C	I	S	T		B	O	U	R	N
A		B		D		T		I		E		M		I
I	R	E	N	I	C	S		C	A	L	L	B	O	X
N		S		O		U		E		L		E		O
	C	O	M	M	O	N	O	R	G	A	R	D	E	N

66

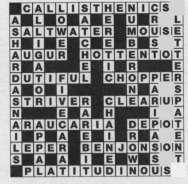

	C	A	L	L	I	S	T	H	E	N	I	C	S	
A		L		O		A		E		U		R		L
S	A	L	T	W	A	T	E	R		M	O	U	S	E
H		I		E		C		E		B		S		T
A	U	G	U	R		H	O	T	T	E	N	T	O	T
R		A				E		I		R				E
D	U	T	I	F	U	L		C	H	O	P	P	E	R
A		O		I						N		A		S
S	T	R	I	V	E	R		C	L	E	A	R	U	P
N				E		A		H				I		A
A	R	A	U	C	A	R	I	A		D	E	P	O	T
I		P		A		E		I		R		A		E
L	E	P	E	R		B	E	N	J	O	N	S	O	N
S		A		A		I		E		W		S		T
	P	L	A	T	I	T	U	D	I	N	O	U	S	

67

P	A	S	S	I	N	G		S	T	R	A	N	G	E
	N		E		A		T		H		M		R	
S	T	O	W		S	C	H	O	O	L	B	O	O	K
	E		E		C		O		M		R		C	
E	N	T	R	E	E		R	E	A	S	O	N	E	D
	N				N		O		S		S		R	
R	A	B	B	I	T	R	U	N		L	I	B	Y	A
			R				G				A			
S	W	E	E	P		C	H	U	B	B	L	O	C	K
	O		A		S		G		R				O	
C	O	C	K	A	T	O	O		E	N	C	O	R	E
	M		F		O		I		A		O		A	
B	E	D	A	R	K	E	N	E	D		V	I	C	E
	R		S		E		G		T		E		L	
B	A	T	T	E	R	Y		C	H	A	R	G	E	R

68

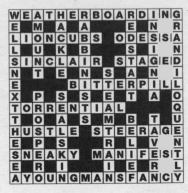

W	E	A	T	H	E	R	B	O	A	R	D	I	N	G
E		M		A		A				E		N		R
L	I	O	N	C	U	B	S		O	D	E	S	S	A
L		U		K		B				S		I		N
S	I	N	C	L	A	I	R		S	T	A	G	E	D
N		T		E		N		S		A		N		I
E					B	I	T	T	E	R	P	I	L	L
X		P		S		S		E		T		A		O
T	O	R	R	E	N	T	I	A	L					Q
T		O		A		S		M		B		T		U
H	U	S	T	L	E		S	T	E	E	R	A	G	E
E		P		S				R		L		V		N
S	N	E	A	K	Y		M	A	N	I	F	E	S	T
E		R		I				I		E		R		L
A	Y	O	U	N	G	M	A	N	S	F	A	N	C	Y

69

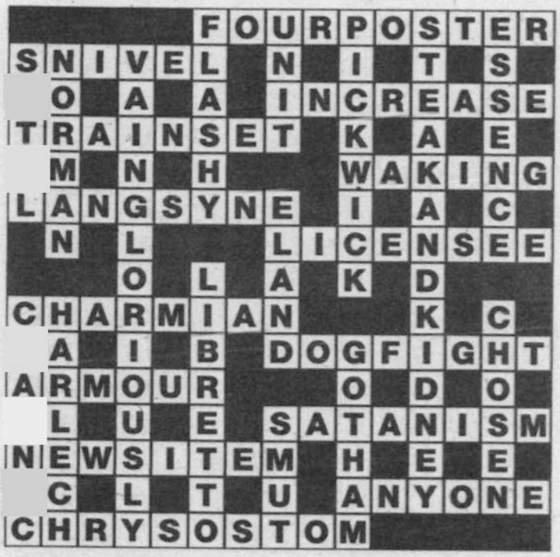
FOURPOSTER
SNIVEL N I T S
O A A INCREASE
TRAINSET K A E
M N H WAKING
LANGSYNE I A C
N L LICENSEE
O L A K D
CHARMIAN K C
A I B DOGFIGHT
ARMOUR O D O
L U E SATANISM
NEWSITEM H E E
C L T U ANYONE
CHRYSOSTOM

70

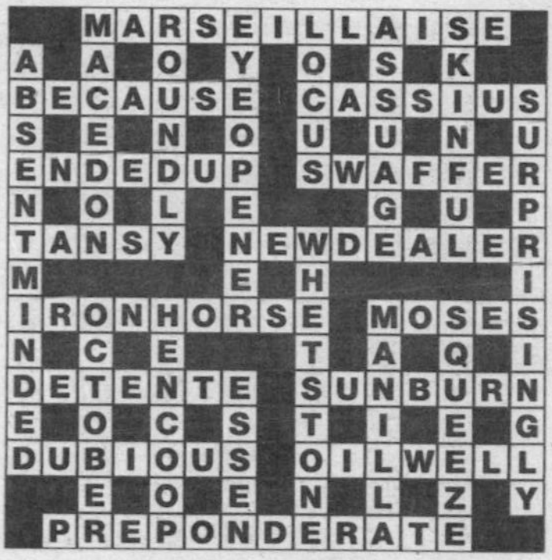
MARSEILLAISE
A A O Y O S K
BECAUSE CASSIUS
S E N O U U N U
ENDEDUP SWAFFER
N O L E G U P
TANSY NEWDEALER
M E H I
IRONHORSE MOSES
N C E T A Q I
DETENTE SUNBURN
E O C S T I E G
DUBIOUS OILWELL
E O E N L Z Y
PREPONDERATE

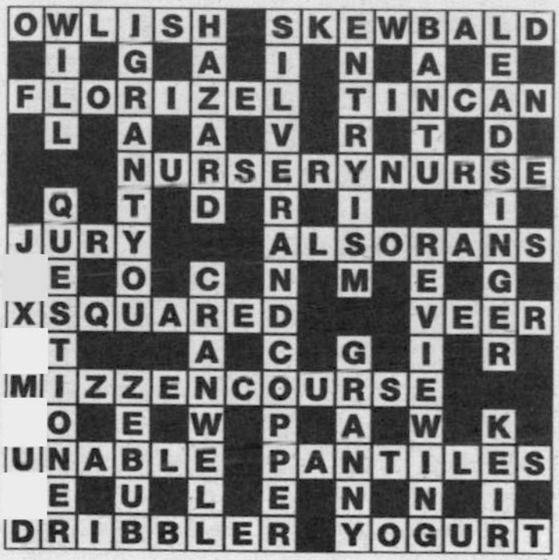
OWLISH SKEWBALD
I G A I N A E
FLORIZEL TINCAN
L A A V R T D
NURSERYNURSE
Q T D R I I
JURY ALSORANS
E O C N M E G
XSQUARED VEER
T A C G I R
MIZZENCOURSE
O E W P A W K
UNABLE PANTILES
E U L E N N I
DRIBBLER YOGURT

71

HARDCASH BARSAC
A I O C R T H
UNTAUGHT XANADU
L C N I C I R
PHOTOSYNTHETIC
D I R M E N H H
ELEGY A C EMERY
S STOKE A
POGES I A PAPER
I U T C N L A D
COMPASSEDROUND
A B N C D A G
BRONZE PRODUCER
L I A O E H A
ENLIST SPARSELY

72

73

ONCEMORE
ATOMIC
IMPOSING
FRIEDEGG
TURBOT
CHESSMAN
OSWESTRY
STUDIOUS
POPINJAY
ORNATE
CARTHAGE
MACARONI
SORDID
CYCLADES

74

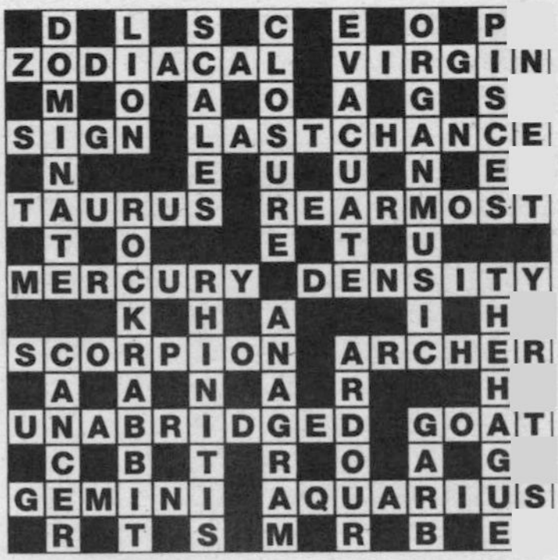
ZODIACAL
VIRGIN
SIGN
LASTCHANCE
TAURUS
REARMOST
MERCURY
DENSITY
SCORPION
ARCHER
UNABRIDGED
GOAT
GEMINI
AQUARIUS

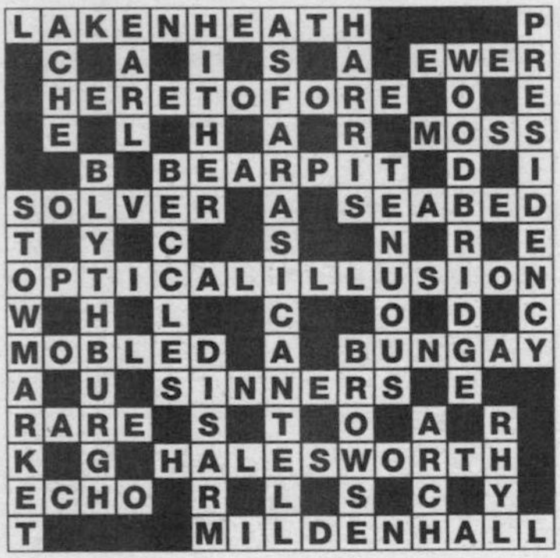
LAKENHEATH
EWER
HERETOFORE
MOSS
BEARPIT
SOLVER
SEABED
OPTICALILLUSION
MOBLED
BUNGAY
SINNERS
RARE
HALESWORTH
ECHO
MILDENHALL

75

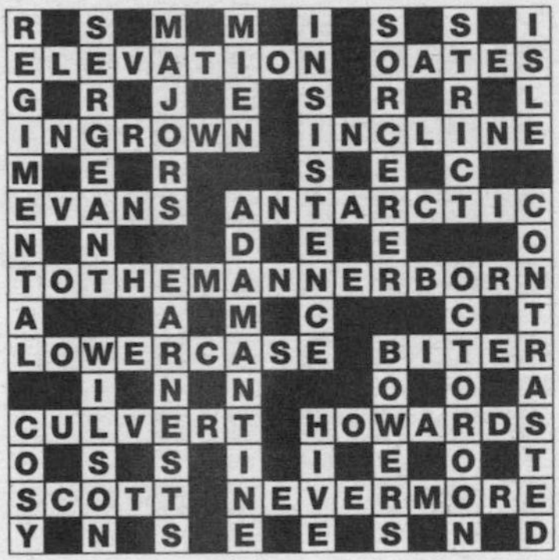
ELEVATION
OATES
INGROWN
INCLINE
EVANS
ANTARCTIC
TOTHEMANNERBORN
LOWERCASE
BITER
CULVERT
HOWARDS
SCOTT
NEVERMORE

76

77

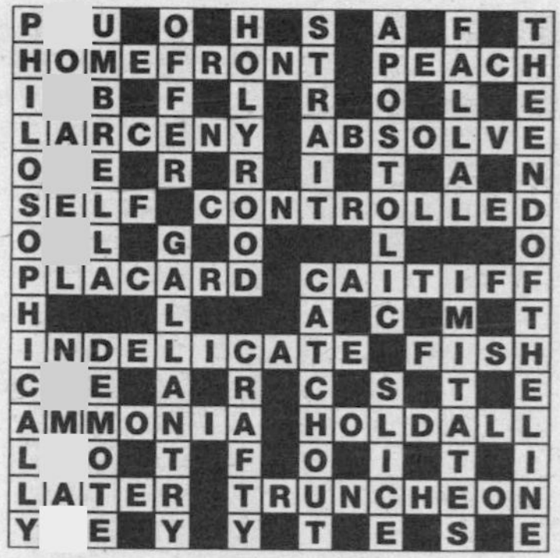
HOMEFRONT PEACH
LARCENY ABSOLVE
SELF CONTROLLED
PLACARD CAITIFF
INDELICATE FISH
AMMONIA HOLDALL
LATER TRUNCHEON

78

DESCRIBE ASLEEP
MADRIGAL ALBION
SPLIT KERBDRILL
FREUDIANSLIP
ENTERPRISING
FUNICULAR NORTH
ELATED SEMITONE
PLEASE ONLYJUST

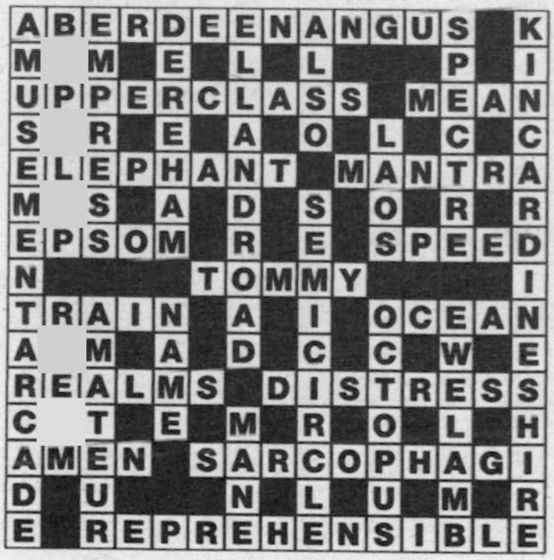
ABERDEENANGUS
UPPERCLASS MEAN
ELEPHANT MANTRA
EPSOM SPEED
TOMMY
TRAIN OCEAN
REALMS DISTRESS
AMEN SARCOPHAGI
REPREHENSIBLE

79

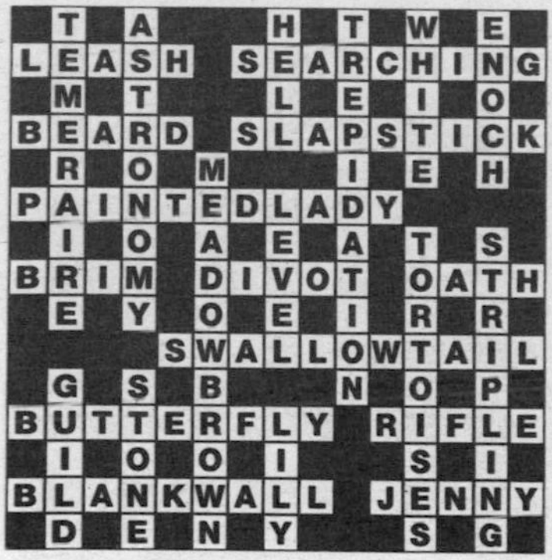
LEASH SEARCHING
BEARD SLAPSTICK
PAINTEDLADY
BRIM DIVOT OATH
SWALLOWTAIL
BUTTERFLY RIFLE
BLANKWALL JENNY

80

81

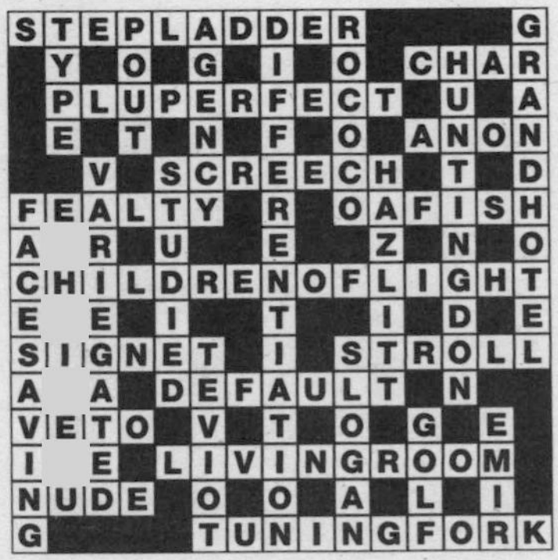
STEPLADDER
CHAR
PLUPERFECT
ANON
SCREECH
FEALTY
OAFISH
CHILDRENOFLIGHT
SIGNET
STROLL
DEFAULT
VETO
LIVINGROOM
NUDE
TUNINGFORK

82

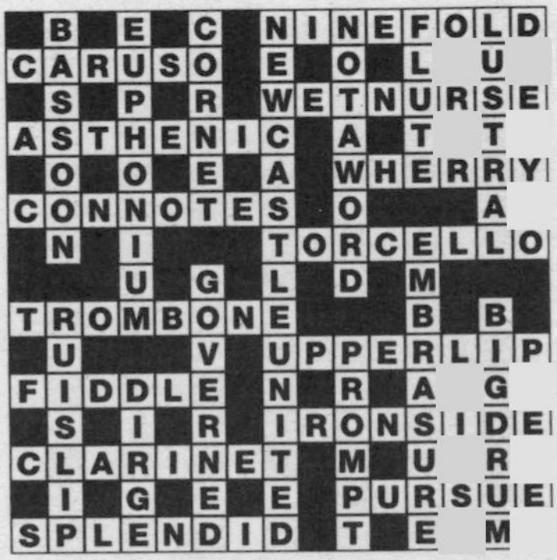
NINEFOLD
CARUSO
WETNURSE
ASTHENIC
WHERRY
CONNOTES
TORCELLO
TROMBONE
UPPERLIP
FIDDLE
IRONSIDE
CLARINET
PURSUE
SPLENDID

VANDIEMENSLAND
RINTINTIN
BATHE
LAPSE
BILLYGOAT
TENTACLE
STODGE
LOCATE
BOTSWANA
EXPATIATE
AMONG
SCION
PIKESTAFF
GETOUTANDABOUT

ONTHEHOP
GOAWAY
HEIFER
CASTLOTS
MENU
BUFFOONERY
EDITORS
PERFUME
INTOLERANT
ROME
PERJURED
ATWORK
GALLIC
KINGLEAR

83

84

85

M	A	N	I	F	E	S	T	A	T	I	O	N	S	
I		O		R		W		N		N		U		C
L	I	N	E	A	G	E		G	O	F	O	R	T	H
K		P		C		A		U		R		S		I
I	S	L	E	T		T	A	L	K	A	T	I	V	E
N		U		I		E		A				N		F
G	A	S	H	O	L	D	E	R		L	O	G	I	C
M				U						I				O
A	S	H	E	S		S	T	E	A	M	I	R	O	N
C		O				C		L		E		E		S
H	O	L	Y	G	R	A	I	L		G	R	A	F	T
I		S		L		R		I		R		G		A
N	E	T	B	A	L	L		P	R	O	V	E	R	B
E		E		S		E		S		V		N		L
	G	R	A	S	P	T	H	E	N	E	T	T	L	E

86

P	R	E	L	U	D	E		C	O	H	A	B	I	T
E		N		N		I		O		U		E		I
T	I	G	E	R		D	E	L	I	G	H	T	E	D
R		I		A		E		O		O		R		I
O	M	N	I	V	O	R	O	U	S		F	A	W	N
L		E		I				R		A		Y		E
				S	T	E	P	F	A	T	H	E	R	S
A		H		H		F		U		T		D		S
P	L	A	Y	E	D	F	A	L	S	E				
P		N		D		L				N		A		P
A	I	D	E		T	U	R	N	T	U	R	T	L	E
R		I		E		V		I		A		T		L
E	X	C	U	R	S	I	O	N		T	R	I	A	L
N		A		G		U		T		E		L		E
T	A	P	R	O	O	M		H	Y	D	R	A	N	T

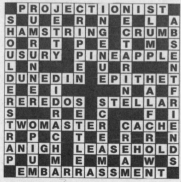

87

	P	R	O	J	E	C	T	I	O	N	I	S	T	
S		U		E		R		N		E		L		A
H	A	M	S	T	R	I	N	G		C	R	U	M	B
O		R		T		P		E		T		M		S
U	S	U	R	Y		P	I	N	E	A	P	P	L	E
L		N				E		U		R				N
D	U	N	E	D	I	N		E	P	I	T	H	E	T
E		E		I						N		A		F
R	E	R	E	D	O	S		S	T	E	L	L	A	R
S				R		E		C				F		I
T	W	O	M	A	S	T	E	R		C	A	C	H	E
R		P		C		T		E		R		R		N
A	N	I	G	H		L	E	A	S	E	H	O	L	D
P		U		M		E		M		A		W		S
	E	M	B	A	R	R	A	S	S	M	E	N	T	

88

H	O	R	N	P	I	P	E		I	C	E	C	A	P
A		O		L		E				H		O		A
M	U	D	G	U	A	R	D		D	I	S	M	A	L
I		E		T		S		S		E		P		I
T	A	N	G	O		P	L	U	S	F	O	U	R	S
E		T		C		I		P				T		A
			C	R	I	C	K	E	T	F	I	E	L	D
S		P		A		A		R		A		R		E
I	N	A	R	T	I	C	U	L	A	T	E			
S		R				I		A		H		V		S
T	I	T	F	O	R	T	A	T		E	L	I	O	T
E		I		U		Y		I		A		E		R
R	I	S	I	N	G		E	V	I	D	E	N	C	E
L		A		C				E		E		N		S
Y	O	N	D	E	R		U	S	E	D	C	A	R	S

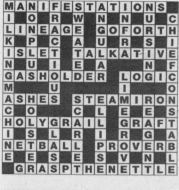

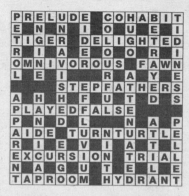

89

					P	R	O	V	E	N	A	N	C	E
I	C	I	C	L	E		U		X		C		O	
	A		O		T		S	P	A	R	K	I	N	G
A	D	J	U	T	A	N	T		M		N		N	
	D		N		R				I	R	O	N	I	C
B	I	R	T	H	D	A	Y		N		W		N	
	S		R				I	D	E	O	L	O	G	Y
			Y		S		E		R		E			
D	U	M	B	B	E	L	L				D		S	
	N		U		A		D	E	L	E	G	A	T	E
S	T	U	M	P	S				A		M		A	
	R		P		H		O	D	D	M	E	N	T	S
D	U	C	K	S	O	U	P		D		N		U	
	T		I		R		A		E	N	T	R	E	E
C	H	A	N	C	E	L	L	O	R					

90

	H		M				E		D		L		Y	
R	E	G	A	L		A	D	I	A	B	A	T	I	C
	X		R				D		M		R		P	
G	A	M	M	A		X	Y	L	O	G	R	A	P	H
	G		A		C				N		Y		Y	
W	O	O	D	W	O	R	K	E	R	S				
	N		U		N		E		U		T		P	
J	A	C	K		S	I	M	O	N		I	V	E	S
	L		E		T		P		Y		M		R	
				B	A	R	T	H	O	L	O	M	E	W
	O		Z		N				N		T		G	
V	A	L	E	N	T	I	N	E		U	H	U	R	U
	V		N		I		O				E		I	
F	E	R	D	I	N	A	N	D		Q	U	I	N	T
	S		A		E		E				S		E	

91

		B	L	A	C	K	A	N	D	B	L	U	E	
P		O		P		E		A		A		N		
R	A	N	C	O	U	R		K	I	N	G	C	U	P
I		D		L		B		E		Q		L		A
Z	E	A	L	O	U	S		D	O	U	C	E	L	Y
E		G		G		T				E		A		A
F	I	E	R	Y		O	V	E	R	T	U	R	E	S
I						N		X						Y
G	O	L	D	C	R	E	S	T		H	O	W	S	O
H		E		A				R		E		A		U
T	O	P	K	N	O	T		A	T	L	A	R	G	E
E		A		N		A		C		L		P		A
R	I	N	G	O	F	F		T	H	I	N	A	I	R
		T		C		F		O		O		T		N
	M	O	N	K	E	Y	W	R	E	N	C	H		

92

	B	A	P	T	I	S	M	O	F	F	I	R	E	
F		T		R		P				O		U		W
R	E	R	O	U	T	E		C	O	R	E	L	L	I
I		O		L		N		H		G		E		T
G	Y	P	S	Y		S	C	A	R	E	C	R	O	W
H		H						R		T				A
T	H	I	E	F		B	E	A	R	F	R	U	I	T
F		E		I		R		D		U		R		E
U	N	D	E	R	S	I	D	E		L	A	T	E	R
L				S		G						I		S
N	I	C	O	T	I	A	N	A		R	E	C	U	R
E		H		H		N		L		O		A		A
S	E	A	W	A	R	D		L	A	T	E	R	A	N
S		I		L				A		O		I		D
	O	N	E	F	O	R	T	H	E	R	O	A	D	

93

H	U	M	O	R	I	S	T		S	C	R	E	A	M
O		A		E		Q				A		V		E
G	R	I	E	V	O	U	S		I	M	P	E	N	D
S		G		I		A				B		S		D
	P	R	O	V	O	S	T	M	A	R	S	H	A	L
A		E		A		H		A		I		A		E
N	A	T	A	L		C		N		C	O	M	U	S
E					B	O	O	T	H					O
M	I	G	H	T		U		L		F	O	R	U	M
O		O		I		R		E		R		E		E
M	A	D	A	M	E	T	U	S	S	A	U	D	S	
E		L		B				H		G		O		H
T	H	E	O	R	Y		P	E	D	I	C	U	R	E
E		S		E				L		L		B		A
R	U	S	T	L	E		A	F	F	E	C	T	E	D

94

M	A	K	E	L	O	V	E	N	O	T	W	A	R	
A		N		E		I		O		U		F		
R	H	O	D	A		S	E	N	I	L	I	T	Y	
S		L		V		I		S		I		E		G
A	I	L	M	E	N	T		T	A	P	E	R	E	R
N				S		O		O				M		E
D	O	S	E	D		R	E	P	R	O	B	A	T	E
V		Y		E						V		T		K
E	U	M	E	N	I	D	E	S		E	T	H	I	C
N		P				R		E		R				A
U	N	H	A	P	P	Y		A	R	S	E	N	A	L
S		O		L		C		C		H		O		E
	I	N	C	A	M	E	R	A		O	N	I	O	N
		I		T		L		L		O		S		D
	S	C	H	O	O	L	O	F	A	T	H	E	N	S

95

M	O	Z	A	M	B	I	Q	U	E					C
	V		C		O		U		A		S	T	A	R
	E	N	T	H	U	S	I	A	S	T		H		O
	R		S		G		N		T		I	R	A	Q
		T		C	H	E	Q	U	E	S		E		U
F	O	R	M	A	T		U		R	E	V	E	R	E
A		A		R			A			T		B		T
C	O	V	E	R	I	N	G	L	E	T	T	E	R	S
E		E		O			E			L		L		E
P	O	L	I	T	E		N		Z	E	A	L	O	T
O		L		S	A	L	A	Z	A	R		S		
W	E	E	K		R		R		M		L		A	
D		R		S	C	R	I	B	B	L	I	N	G	
E	A	S	T		A		A		I		A		U	
R					P	A	N	T	A	G	R	U	E	L

96

S		S		L		W		P		E		T		S
L	I	Q	U	E	F	I	E	R		G	R	O	U	P
I		U		A		N		O		G		W		A
D	E	A	D	D	O	G		C	A	P	T	A	I	N
E		D		E				U		L		R		
R	A	R	E	R		C	O	M	M	A	N	D	E	R
U		O				O		B		N				U
L	A	N	T	E	R	N	L	E	C	T	U	R	E	S
E				T		V		N				O		H
S	O	U	T	H	E	A	S	T		P	L	U	S	H
		P		N		L				E		G		O
A	I	R	V	I	C	E		M	A	R	S	H	A	L
B		O		C		S		I		S		T		D
L	L	A	M	A		C	O	M	M	O	D	O	R	E
E		R		L		E		E		N		N		R

97 **98**

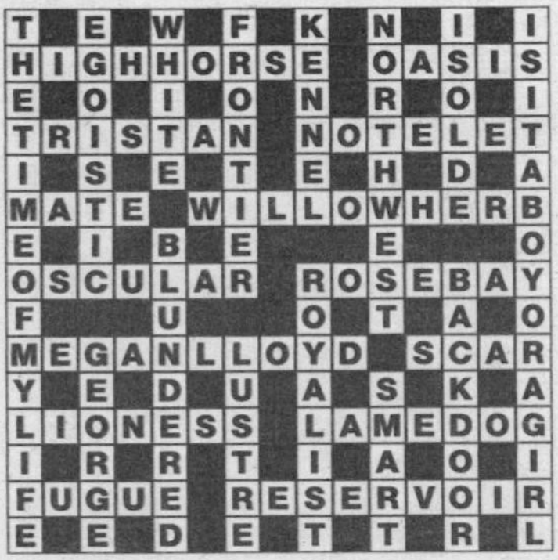

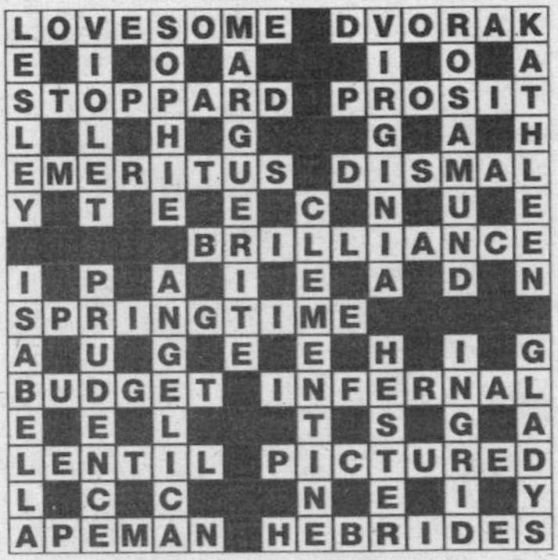

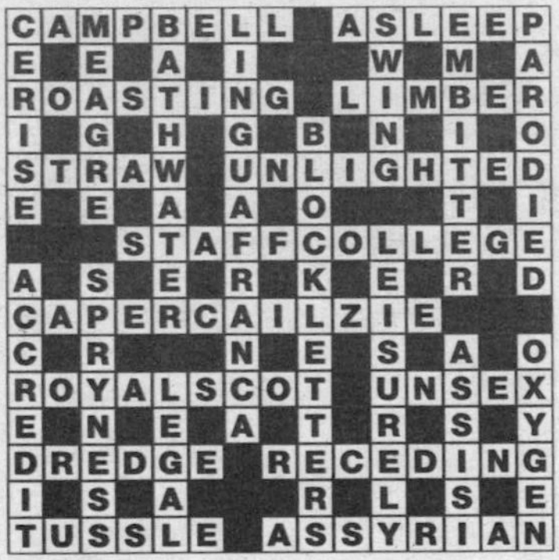

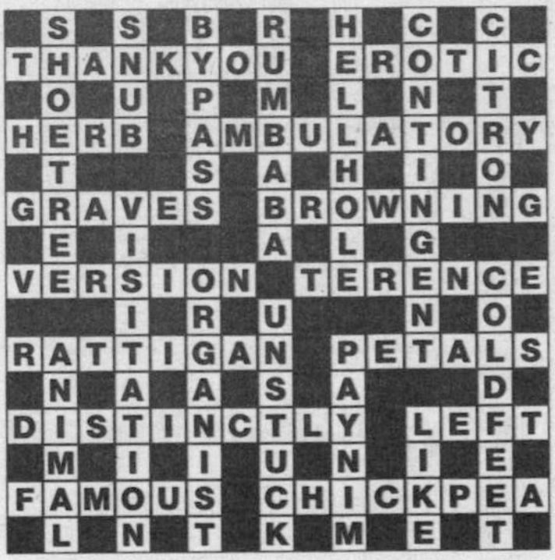

99 **100**

'How can anything so fiendish be so much fun?'
SIMON HOGGART

The **Guardian**

monkey puzzles

**THE ULTIMATE CRYPTIC
CROSSWORD COLLECTION**

ARAUCARIA

The **Guardian**

£5.99 • ISBN 1 84354 004 5

a or an before h? use an only if the h is silent: an hour, an heir, an honourable man, an honest woman; but a hero, a hotel, a historian (but don't change a direct quote if the speaker says, for example, "an historic") • **abattoir** • **abbeys** cap up, eg Rievaulx Abbey, Westminster Abbey • **Aborigines, Aboriginal** cap up when referring to native Australians • **aborigines, aboriginal** lc when referring to indigenous populations • **accents** use on French, German, Spanish and Irish Gaelic words (but not anglicised French words such as cafe, apart from exposé, resumé) • **access** has been known as contact since the 1989 Children Act • **acknowledgment** not acknowledgement • **acronyms** take initial cap, eg Aids, Isa, Mori, Nato • **act** uc when using full name, eg Criminal Justice Act 1998, Official Secrets Act; but lc on second reference, eg "the act", and when speaking in more general terms, eg "we need a radical freedom of information act"; bills remain lc until passed into law • **acting** always lc: acting prime minister, acting committee chair, etc • **actor** male and female: avoid actress except when in name of award, eg Oscar for best actress. One 27-year-old actor contacted the Guardian to say "actress" has acquired a faintly pejorative tinge and she wants people to call her actor (except for her agent who should call her often) • **AD, BC** AD goes before the date (AD64), BC goes after (300BC); both go after the century, eg second century AD, fourth century BC • **adaptation** not adaption • **addendum** plural addendums • **addresses** 119 Farringdon Road, London EC1R 3ER •

> **'This stuff matters. Rules do not limit; they liberate'**
> **John Humphrys**

> **'Valuably insists on the writing of good English'**
> **Tom Paulin**

The Guardian Stylebook
ISBN 1843549913 Price £9.99